THE
COLLECTED PAPERS
OF
WILFRED TROTTER
F.R.S.

OXFORD MEDICAL PUBLICATIONS

THE
COLLECTED PAPERS
OF
WILFRED TROTTER
F.R.S.

OXFORD UNIVERSITY PRESS
LONDON : HUMPHREY MILFORD

OXFORD UNIVERSITY PRESS
AMEN HOUSE, E.C. 4
London Edinburgh Glasgow New York
Toronto Melbourne Capetown Bombay
Calcutta Madras
HUMPHREY MILFORD
PUBLISHER TO THE UNIVERSITY

FIRST PUBLISHED 1941
REPRINTED 1942

PRINTED IN GREAT BRITAIN

INTRODUCTION

SHORTLY before his death in November 1939, my father formed the intention of republishing, and perhaps adding to, the ten essays which are presented in this book. All but one of them were originally prepared as addresses to various medical bodies, and they deal mainly with what may be called the philosophy of medicine. The tenth essay, entitled 'Has the intellect a function?', gives a glimpse of the subject which occupied his mind in the last years. This was the problem of how the human mind could be made into an instrument of greater practical use, and the solution which he evolved is embodied in the striking phrase—'the calibration of the intellect'. If his health had allowed him to elaborate this idea it might have proved his most considerable achievement.

The war came when he was already laid low by his last illness. This latest evidence of the incompatibility of the English and German peoples could not fail to stimulate him, and it produced the two slight works which end this volume. It seems not altogether inappropriate to present at this time the last thoughts of the author of *Instincts of the Herd in Peace and War*.

W. R. TROTTER

March, 1941

CONTENTS

EMERGENCY[1]

WE have all of us read many times in the newspaper account of an accident some such words as these —'a doctor was sent for but unfortunately before he arrived life was extinct'. To some of us in our youth, when even the hospital was only an ambition, these words were of great power. How wonderful, we felt, to belong to a profession whose members were able almost by their mere presence to influence such issues, and might hope as it were to beat off Death even as he stooped to strike. During our student days these dreams began perhaps a little to fade, and we sometimes wondered when we were to learn of these ideal and, as we had supposed, not infrequent emergencies in which we were to stand confidently between life and death. With increasing experience there has disclosed itself the situation on which I am to make some general remarks.

With whatever romantic notions we enter upon the practice of medicine, we shall probably find when we are actually engaged in it that but a small part of our time is taken up by the desperate or even the moderately urgent emergency. Nevertheless, it may be said without undue straining of the phrase that in a certain sense the whole of a doctor's life is passed in a medium from which the pressure of emergency is never remote. He may be described, perhaps not too extravagantly, as living to some degree like a soldier in an unfriendly country, where his whole behaviour must be alert and circumspect, and his reaction to events under careful control. To define more clearly this aspect of the doctor's

[1] Address to Senior Students and Junior Practitioners, published with acknowledgements to the *University College Hospital Magazine*. Reprinted from *Medical World*, 6 Oct. 1933.

situation let me remind you of some features that are not
always remembered, first in the relation between him
and his patients, and secondly of his position in the social
scheme.

PATIENT AND DOCTOR

When a doctor supplies his patient with treatment
and earns his fee, the transaction does not and never can
possess the enviable simplicity of that between trades-
man and customer, when in return for the appropriate
price a pound of some commodity is handed across the
counter. The attitude of the patient approaching his
doctor must always be tinged—for the most part unconsciously—with distaste and dread; its deepest desire
will tend to be comfort and relief rather than cure, and
its faith and expectation will be directed towards some
magical exhibition of these boons. Do not let yourselves
believe that however smoothly concealed by education,
by reason, and by confidential frankness these strong
elements may be, they are ever in any circumstances
altogether absent.

The doctor on his part is perhaps dimly aware of the
strange mixture of distrust and inordinate expectation
that the patient unconsciously entertains; he knows,
moreover, how feeble are the resources against disease
he commands, and he knows that for the reconciliation
of these two incompatibles the responsibility will rest
on him and his personal moral force.

Phenomena of this imponderable kind are always
exaggerated in the very fact of being described, and
falsified in the very fact of definition. The crude sketch
of them I have attempted will therefore seem rather
unreal unless it is received with sympathetic understanding. It does, however, embody a reality of which

every doctor should be aware. Thus only can he understand and perhaps avert the unreasonable explosions of
hostility and censure to which in some degree every
member of his profession is exposed; thus only can he
preserve himself from the unhealthy reactions to which
his situation contains such inducements. For if he denies
himself clear insight into realities, he will always be in
danger of seeking protection in solemnity and pompous
reserve on the one hand, or on the other in the cheap
and profitable garment of mere bustle and bounce.

Public and Doctor

An established profession that forms a recognized
part of the social structure might be supposed to depend
on a fair balance between its duties and its privileges—
between, on the one hand, the things its members alone
are compelled to do, and on the other hand, the things its
members alone are allowed to be. Now the medical
profession is unique in the extent to which in the establishment of its social position this equitable balance has
been neglected.

The senior professions of the Church and Law have
always had prestige enough to enable each of them to
keep a finger firmly and consistently in the governmental
pie. They have therefore been able to see to it that any
duty that was laid upon them should be set off by a
corresponding privilege or immunity. The lowly and
junior profession of Medicine, unlike its proud and elder
sisters, has had no direct part and no direct influence in
the work of government. It has therefore had to submit
to its duties being piled up as occasion, arose, with no
resource for securing a due compensation of privilege
and immunity except such slender sense of natural justice
as governments possess, and their occasional doubts

about the prudence of overloading a willing beast. These resources have shown all the ineffectiveness we might have expected. The result is that at a time when it is no longer possible to conceal the wholly unique importance of medicine for the very existence of social life, that profession finds itself of all professions the least in command of social prestige, the least privileged, the most exposed, and the hardest worked.

I do not mention this state of affairs because I think it is to be deplored. I do not think it is to be deplored. The evolutionary course that has put the profession of medicine where it is may not be the one that would have been pursued by conscious wisdom, but it has had the result of putting medicine in the very small class of professions that, in this tame world, can still be called jobs for men. When I speak of jobs for men, I use a traditional phrase that nowadays needs a little definition. By it I mean professions in which it is possible for people —men or women—to pursue the dying ideal that an occupation for adults should allow of intellectual freedom, should give character as much chance as cleverness, and should be subject to the tonic of difficulty and the spice of danger.

When I put it forward as a recommendation that medicine is a dangerous trade, I do not of course refer to those physical dangers of which the general public so much likes to take the romantic view. The possibility that a medical man may meet physical disaster as a direct result of his work is no doubt perceptible; it does in its minor degree perhaps contribute to the moral respectability of the occupation, but it is not in any way relevant to my theme. The practice of medicine is dangerous in a more interesting and more pressing sense than that, first, because it is so meagrely cared for by legal privi-

lege and immunity and, secondly, because of the inherent difficulty and instability of the relation of patient and doctor.

It is considerations such as these that justify the statement I have made, that in a certain sense of the term the feeling of emergency can never be far from the mind of the active doctor. However disturbing that experience may be, and however much at times he may be inclined to envy the calm and prestige of more secure professions, if he is a person who prefers having a man's job to having one of the other kind, he will remember that his deficiency and his exposure are the price to be paid for that dignity.

The Emergencies of Practice

When we turn to consider the emergencies in the strict sense of the term with which the doctor has to deal, we find we are still in a region where personality at least holds its own in comparison with technical equipment. For the more urgent the call for decision and action, the more important are character, the slowly matured power of judgement and a grasp of fundamental principle, and the less trustworthy are mere detailed knowledge and executive skill. It is for this reason only that it is possible to have the hope of saying anything useful on such a topic and on such an occasion. These are not circumstances that permit systematic exposition, and my much humbler purpose is to recall a few simple and general principles which I think should be the very foundation of our mental attitude in approaching urgent work.

The Kinds of Emergency

No one can be a satisfactory craftsman who does not possess what we vaguely call a feeling for his material—

an intuitive understanding of what it will resist and what it will yield to, of its grain and temper, of when it can be commanded and when it must be coaxed. That most difficult of all materials, the living body, naturally does not call for less of such sympathetic comprehension than do metal and wood and stone. Now if we have any degree of this quality we cannot but feel that any surgical operation, however exquisitely carried out, and even in the hands of the greatest masters, has in it an element of the crude and violent. That we are all convinced of the beneficence of modern operative surgery need not blind us to the recognition of this patent fact. It is, however, far more important to recognize that an operation, apart from consideration of its ultimate object, is not only in itself an injurious event, but one which is likely to disturb or even arrest what reparative process nature has already in hand against the disease which the operation is designed to attack.

This consideration brings us to recognize a principle quite essential to the attitude of mind in which an urgent surgical case should be approached. Certain conditions find the body defenceless or at once break through and overwhelm any defence it may attempt. In dealing with them we are therefore *wholly* dependent on what, if anything, surgery can do, and need have no scruples about compromising any defensive or reparative process of nature's own. Success is then to be obtained only through promptitude of action and good workmanship ruthlessly applied. These are the *absolute emergencies*. They include such conditions as haemorrhage from the larger arteries, foreign bodies lodged in the air passages or gullet, acute intestinal obstruction, the graver abdominal injuries, the grosser abdominal perforations. In the broad sense the handling of them is relatively

simple. It demands a certain capacity to recognize plain facts, and the supreme surgical virtue of resolution, but it involves no doubts and fears as to what should be attempted, and no balancing between the virtues of art and nature, for nature is already defeated.

ABSOLUTE AND RELATIVE EMERGENCIES

It needs but little experience, however, to show that the class of absolute emergencies is a comparatively small one. Very many injuries and diseases not immediately fatal set up at once processes of resistance or repair effective enough to attenuate the lesion more or less largely. When such a process is present it brings the case into the class of what we may call *relative emergencies*. In this class the fundamental problem of surgical treatment has lost the simplicity it possesses in absolute emergencies. An operation, apart from inflicting an injury of its own, tends to disturb or destroy what natural defensive or reparative process may be at work. The cardinal problem therefore becomes what shall be the relation of the treatment adopted to this natural process. Three relations are possible. First, the treatment may be extirpative and radical, getting rid of the disease at one sweep. In these circumstances—which may be illustrated by the early operation for acute appendicitis—the cure is obtained in spite of, and is apparently uninfluenced by, what damage the interference inflicts on the natural resistance to the disease. Secondly, the treatment may have to proceed in close alliance with the natural process, and its success will depend on the scrupulous minuteness with which the process is respected and used. Such is the law under which all operations for advanced and developed appendicitis must be conducted, and any serious breach of it will be punished

by the endangering of the patient's life. Thirdly, the treatment may have to be purely auxiliary to the natural process, leaving the essential struggle to be fought out between the disease and the body's resistance, and interfering only after the crisis is past to hasten recovery. This is the method to which we are limited in many spreading infections. Such conditions are essentially conflicts between an invading organism and the resistance of the body, and are far less capable of being influenced, except perhaps for the worse, than is still optimistically supposed by energetic surgeons. You cannot kill microbes with a scalpel. When, however, the infection has been conquered, there is no more beneficent agent in, so to say, cleaning up the battle-field by opening the consequent residual abscesses. It is highly probable, for example, that the orthodox treatment of a spreading cellulitis by multiple incisions is without influence on the extension of the disease. I do not say it is without effect, for it gratifies the urge towards action of patient and doctor, and it doubtless increases the destructive changes in the tissues, but it has nothing to say whether the infection is to spread or be arrested, for that issue is decided by factors far beyond the reach of any knife.

In dealing with what I have called the relative emergencies, it is necessary, then, deliberately to choose the category of treatment to be adopted in the given case and, in reason, to stick to it. For in an atmosphere of urgency even simple ideas are subject to confusion, and confusion of thought inevitably leads to confusion in action. Now it is obvious that in order to be able to make this choice with rational confidence we must have some practical idea of what the natural powers of resistance and repair can do.

The Strength of the Natural Process

Nature has been kind to the surgeon. She has equipped the body with a wonderful series of bilateral and of quasi-superfluous organs which seem veritably to invite the knife. But she has done a great deal more than that for him; she has given the body powers of resistance and recovery by which the whole of his work is conditioned and made possible. Making use of these in his every act, he is perhaps inclined a little ungratefully to neglect the study of them when circumstances compel him to rely on them chiefly or alone. Now in order to use these natural powers to the full we must get an understanding of the exact conditions under which their strength is developed, and the often unexpected ways in which we may, in all innocence, interfere with their action. I have already referred to the natural resistance to infections; let me illustrate my present point by a few words about the natural control of haemorrhage.

Haemorrhage is of all symptoms perhaps the most appalling to the patient, and the most trying to the nerve of the doctor. If we are to prevent, therefore, the sick room in which it occurs from becoming the scene of mere flustered inefficiency, we must be ready with a system of clear and precise ideas for handling such a situation.

Let us first clear the ground by certain eliminations. I have already classified haemorrhage from the larger arteries as an absolute emergency. Haemorrhage from an external wound and intra-abdominal haemorrhage, on account of the certainty of surgical treatment, should go into the same category. We are left then with three common types—epistaxis, haemoptysis, and haematemesis—which are relative emergencies in which we

must rely chiefly, if not wholly, on the natural resources of the body.

There is probably no more ancient and deeply contrived function than the natural control of haemorrhage, and its capabilities are truly astonishing. They are, however, often under-estimated, because they demand the exact fulfilment of certain conditions which are frequently with the best of intentions made impossible. These conditions are that the pressure within the bleeding vessel should be kept low and that the site of the bleeding-point should be absolutely at rest. It is odd how difficult it is to get this simple principle understood, and the simple instructions that follow from it rigorously carried out. Conscientious nurse and anxious relative will conspire, the one to wash and the other to feed, in spite of categorical orders that nothing must be done or given, and exceptions to this rule will be taken for granted unless expressly forbidden.

We are concerned here only with principles, and I shall but mention the one concrete example of severe epistaxis. Supposing you wish to make a serious attempt in such a case to avoid the recognized but odious alternative of plugging the nose, and to give natural arrest a real chance, this is the procedure to follow. Prop the patient well up with a comfortable inclination to one side, arrange a large pad of wool for him to dribble into, put a dental prop between the teeth, *forbid him to breathe through the nose or to swallow*, and give a substantial dose of morphia. Only by mouth breathing and a complete cessation of swallowing can the bleeding area be given the necessary and almost infallibly haemostatic rest. We must not, however, allow ourselves to become entangled among details, for my purpose is merely to define general considerations on which to build our attitude towards

emergency work. We have seen that one of our chief tasks is to determine in a given case how much we can work in accord with natural processes, and when we are compelled to disregard them. It is natural to ask then how much time we can give ourselves to determine these matters.

Degrees of Urgency

Surgeons have long preached the need for early operation in urgent cases, and I do not think the time has come when they can safely remit their pressure in this direction. It is perhaps true, however, that a slight enlargement of that formula is now to be desired, and that we should press that, in every such case, the patient should at the earliest possible moment be put in conditions where any operation that may become necessary can be most safely and quickly performed. If we put the whole stress on the operation itself, we may be in danger of creating an atmosphere of false urgency in which diagnosis and due preparation of the patient are likely to suffer, and mere bustle takes the place of surgical promptitude and resolution.

In almost every case there is at our disposal a certain margin of time in which preparation and reflection can proceed with rational composure. Moreover, deliberate delay in the interests of diagnosis is sometimes imperative. Let me return again to the commonest of all abdominal emergencies. The best treatment of acute appendicitis is operation within the first twenty-four hours. In this statement there is, of course, implicit the assumption of correct diagnosis, and the time limit named is usually ample to make that reasonably assured. If we try to cut it down very much, we shall be running an increasing risk of making diagnostic mistakes. It is

sometimes said that in a doubtful case of appendicitis it is safest to operate. That doctrine is a precarious one. It has led to unnecessary operations, it has led to operations wrongly directed, and it has led to useless operations being done in circumstances when any operation is actively harmful. There cannot be a worse blunder, for example, than to operate, as has often been done for a supposed appendicitis, in a case of oncoming pneumonia.

Another illustration of what we may fairly call a false sense of urgency is to be found in a not uncommon attitude towards the surgery of head injuries. Apart from penetrating, and presumably contaminated, wounds of the brain which are absolute emergencies, the head injuries of civil practice rarely call for urgent operation. The capacity of the brain to recover from extensive contusion and minor haemorrhages is very great; but its susceptibility to suffer gravely in this state from the further damage of an operation is no less pronounced, so that an unnecessary operation is a far more serious blunder than in most abdominal cases. The progressive local haemorrhage is the only condition that produces a surgical emergency. It is comparatively rare, its symptoms display an orderly development, and permit of reasoned diagnosis and rational treatment. It is thus possible to say that operation within the first twenty-four hours is almost always useless and dangerous, and we may add without extravagance that the very few patients who survive would have done better without it. Thus once more is enforced the lesson that urgent cases call for the special exercise of rational foresight and prudence. It is in the very nature of surgery to favour the use of active methods, indeed we may suppose people become surgeons in response to a natural inclina-

tion towards action. Popular opinion, with remarkable docility, has come to reinforce this tendency, and to think it must be a poor surgeon who does not do something in every crisis. It is particularly necessary, therefore, for those who possess the admirable temperament of the surgeon, to guard against allowing themselves to mistake mere senseless activity for true surgical determination and promptitude.

It is the penalty of choosing a great theme that the treatment of it is bound to be inadequate. This discrepancy must be especially evident here, for I have used an occasion and a subject both equally important to bring forward considerations so elementary that some of them have probably never occurred to you. In this respect I shall ask you to be indulgent to a weakness of seniority by which it tends to over-estimate the value of the elementary and the simple. With your recent and highly elaborate equipment you will need a special effort of tolerance to get any small profit there may be in the point of view I have expressed.

If we return for a moment to the point from which we started, you will have gathered that I do not share the journalist's view that it usually matters much whether the doctor arrives just before or just after life is extinct. The good doctor does not need to drug his imagination with romantic ideas, but he does supremely need to look upon his situation with regard to the world, his patient, and his technical tasks in a realistic spirit. He will find that the world gives him little attention except to impose restrictions and to exact responsibilities, and he will find his patients but little able to co-operate with him, uneasy and subject to strange moods. But he will not be without consolations: first, the knowledge that its difficulties make his task one fit for grown men in a real world;

and secondly, in co-operation with his single steady friend—the natural power of the body to resist injury and disease. It is in work with this inimitable ally that he will earn his least corruptible reward.

THE COMMEMORATION OF GREAT MEN[1]

I

EVENTS that recur with a regular period are apt to be taken as a matter of course, to have their significance regarded as obvious, and to seem in no need of justification. To resist this tendency to confuse the familiar with the self-evident is one of the most necessary efforts the mind is called upon to make. The institution whose recurrent activity we take part in to-day was set up one hundred and nineteen years ago and marks a birthday since which two hundred and four years have passed. For more than a century orations have been delivered on the life and work of Hunter and they have explored their theme from every aspect and adorned it with every art. The high qualities of these orations make it impossible for a new contributor without special aptitude to hope for any freshness in the presentation of a topic already so well discussed by better men. On the other hand, the imposing length of the series may perhaps have a little obscured our apprehension of the more elementary meanings that underlie these regularly returning occasions. Under the pressure of these converging indications it will be my relatively humble task to seek answers to such questions as the first giver of this oration might be supposed in his preliminary musings to have put to himself. What are the reasons, we shall want to know, why John Hunter should be regarded as a fit subject for enduring celebration, and what do we wish and what do we attain in the many activities by which in general we pursue or

---

[1] Delivered before the Royal College of Surgeons of England, 15 Feb. 1932. Reprinted from the *British Medical Journal*, 20 Feb. 1932.

suppose ourselves to pursue the commemoration of great men?

II

To question established beliefs is nowadays perhaps a rather old-fashioned activity. We may be sure, nevertheless, that it is one of which Hunter would thoroughly have approved even if his own greatness was to be in question. In that case, however, if we are to judge by his known methods in controversy, the discussion would go all the smoother if we hinted beforehand what the verdict was to be. For of the verdict there can be no doubt, and it will find that the makers of this recurring celebration not only chose an exceptionally sound foundation but built perhaps a great deal better than they knew.

Hunter was a successful surgeon with a large practice and a correspondingly ample income. It must not be suggested here that that is anything but highly respectable attainment. It is not, however, attainment that, under any magnification or however many ciphers may be subtracted from the mortality of his patients and added to his income, reveals in its creator the heroic features we are seeking.

Hunter made the museum which for over a century has been the very focus and palladium of this College. In this work we find the giant energy and resolution of true greatness directed by a correspondingly clear and ample idea. It was no mere miscellaneous assemblage of odds and ends as the collections of his contemporaries tended perhaps a little to be, but a grouping of orderly series nobly illustrating the living world and the processes of disease. It is scarcely possible for the richness and order of this historic monument to be spoken of too highly, but it may be doubted whether in themselves

they could have given to their creator his unique and enduring prestige.

Hunter was a consistent and expert user of the experimental method in the study of living processes, and it is on this fact that his fame essentially and ultimately rests. It was by impressing this method on his pupils and successors that his services to science and to surgery have had their most extended and their richest effects.

These experimental studies covered a very wide field and dealt with fundamental problems such as the process of repair, the survival of isolated tissues, transplantation, grafting, inflammation, the processes of growth, and the influence on them of the sexual glands. Such researches were pursued with a characteristic zeal and ability, and yielded results of importance in many directions. It is impossible, however, not to be struck by a certain disproportion between the amount of energy and genius that was expended and the harvest of substantial knowledge that was gathered. Many of the researches were indecisive, not a few of the conclusions were incorrect, and no single advance was won which could be said to mark an epoch in the history of knowledge. Every student of Hunter is convinced that he belonged to the very small class of those who possess powers of the first order; few can be equally convinced that he made a direct contribution to the science of his day fully commensurate with his splendid gifts. It is therefore particularly happy that his commemoration should have been formally assured and entrusted to an enduring institution. Other experimental workers in the science of life, more fortunate but perhaps not more richly endowed, have by their labours so contributed to the very structure and substance of knowledge as to be sure of remembrance without any specific memorial. Of

c

Harvey, of Pasteur, of Lister, every student of physiology or pathology is in some sense the beneficiary and direct legatee. The influence of Hunter was more limited to the indirect and germinal; he did not make an epoch, he founded a school.

III

That Hunter's prodigious powers and devotion yielded such comparatively moderate accessions to knowledge is perhaps not without a certain shade of mystery and pathos. It is an idle occupation for the common man to busy himself with explaining the successes and failures of greatness, but it is no undue presumption to turn our attention to the circumstances of Hunter's life in the search for light upon his career. He was so resolutely modern in his attitude towards the problems of life, and he accepted so whole-heartedly the working hypothesis of their solubility, that we are apt to forget the state of knowledge of his time. During the sixty-five years of Hunter's life, from 1728 to 1793, the biologist could look for practically no help from the sciences of the inorganic, and was without almost every article of equipment we now regard as essential to experimental work.

We are accustomed to associate with the earliest foundations of modern chemistry and physics the great names of Cavendish, Priestley, Galvani, Volta, and Lavoisier. Every one of them was junior to Hunter. Let us for a moment regard the situation of Hunter in his prime in 1765. He would have had to wait ten years for Priestley's discovery of oxygen in 1775; he would have had to wait over sixty years for Wöhler's synthesis of urea and the foundation of biochemistry in 1828, and nearly eighty years for Joule's mechanical equivalent of heat. Over sixty years ahead was Joseph Jackson Lister's

completion of the compound microscope, which made possible the science of histology, and exactly a century away the proof of the nature of wound infections by Lister's greater son.

In this atmosphere of embryonic science and primitive equipment Hunter worked with high faith and energy at problems which have resisted, or yielded only grudgingly to, all the resources of the modern world. Not only was there little help for him in the general body of science but biology itself lay in a certain sense between two tides of inspiration. The gross structure of the animal body had been fully exploited by the great anatomists; the stimulus this had given to knowledge had come to the flood and was ebbing fast. Exact histology lay half a century in the future, and for the want of it most of Hunter's experiments could not be given full exploitation or carried to exact conclusions. It needs all our imaginative sympathy to picture the twilit country in which his labours were carried on—the air is dim and thick, the range of vision short, the appearance of things ambiguous,

> —the tired waves vainly breaking
> Seem here no painful inch to gain.

We can scarcely resist the sense that there was a prophetic element in the feverish energy with which he set himself to his tasks. For events were to give to such work a new value and a new necessity. The long climax of the eighteenth century was passing by. Ahead lay a changed order where social structure would have an unheard-of complication and biological problems an unheard-of urgency. The world seemed to pause, gathering itself for the plunge. The movement would be slow at first but presently would take on a vertiginous acceleration.

In 1774, when Hunter was 46 and in the full tide of
work, a young Scotchman named James Watt left Glasgow for Birmingham to become the partner of Matthew
Boulton and with his help to add to the gathering forces
of the industrial revolution the immense momentum of
the steam-engine. There followed a commercial expansion and a crude industrial hypertrophy which made
this country the envy of the world, but which we can
now contemplate with only a qualified pride. The growth
of trade and population was so imperious and so exuber-
ant that the ordinary hygienic difficulties of social life
increased out of all bounds. Industrial areas of population grew unchecked by regard for space, for decency, or
for health, while the discrepancy between the rate of
development of mechanical and biological knowledge
became more and more dangerously wide. The great,
but as we can now see rather Grecian, gift made by the
North to the South when James Watt brought the steam-
engine to England was to be repaid in a nobler and less
equivocal form when eighty-six years later a young
Englishman named Joseph Lister went to Glasgow. The
Industrial Revolution and the steam-engine had done
their work. To the great new industrial populations
hospitals had become more and more indispensable, and
with every enlargement of their activities they had
become more and more dangerous to their surgical
patients. The process was a progressive one for a reason
that is now obvious, the frequent occurrence of infection
from patient to patient being ideally suited to raising the
virulence of micro-organisms to the highest pitch and
maintaining it there. Surgery in hospitals was in fact
already threatening to become extinct.

It was in this darkest hour that the method of Hunter
brought off its greatest stroke. Of that method Lister

was a devout and explicit disciple. In five years from his going to Glasgow he had solved the problem of wound infection, and modern surgery was born.

The lapse of time, with its slow revelation of perspective and proportion in the succession of events, seems more and more clearly to teach the lesson of Hunter's career. It was not as a surgeon, as the maker of his great museum, or even as a discoverer in science, that his greatness was revealed or his influence perpetuated. It was by his example in the use of the scientific method—faithfully, in purity of heart, and with utter devotion to truth.

IV

We cannot examine even in this hasty way the special instance of a given memorable man without feeling a logical pressure towards the consideration of the more general case, of the meaning and motives that underlie one of the most widespread of human impulses. We assume that the commemoration of heroes is possible and to be desired, and it would perhaps be well in prudence to leave it at that, for the moment we pierce the smooth surface of the assumption we find ourselves in a world of ambiguities and uncomfortable hints. Nevertheless it is perhaps a healthy exercise in an environment such as this—so solid, so stable, so justly confident—to recall to ourselves sharply that these also are appearances.

Let us begin by planting squarely before us the plain fact of death. I make that specious request not in the expectation that it will be granted, for it is in the very nature of that fact's relation to life that we cannot get a square, collected, and as it were binocular look at it. A living mind can form no intimate conception of its own

death, and is apparently for ever incapable of comprising two categories which are not opposites, as is often crudely supposed, but superlatively different. And yet in the world of gross reality the expectation of death for the individual is the one prospect for which the attestation of experience amounts most nearly to philosophic certainty. This radical antinomy in the life of every conscious being, in spite of having been the chief pre-occupation of the speculative mind since it came into existence, remains and must remain unresolved. Among the by-products of these secular activities is the strange jumble of sense and fantasy that makes up our attitude towards the memory of the dead.

In even its most sober and enlightened moments mankind has regarded the dead with fear and pity. In other moments the feeling has risen to awe and reverence, or has sunk to a strange blend of horror and contempt. The mixture of feeling has withdrawn attention from the central fact, that from the moment of a man's death the memory of him begins to fade, for he has entered on a new state about which the only certainty is that it has nothing to do with life. Nothing can arrest this decline, no memorial can do more than delay it and as it delays distort. In all our commemorations, whether by word or by plastic art, we make our own pictures and drift increasingly away from the actual man. These are the real ghosts, and nothing brings more certain conviction of a man's death than his memorial. This steadily increasing divergence between the subject commemorated and the object commemorating has perhaps its consolations when we view the objects of memorial art in our public places. At any rate we may tell ourselves as we shrink before the marble frock-coats and the bronze beards and whiskers, their supposed subjects could

scarcely have been like that. However forlorn in the eyes of mere reason the task of keeping in being the veritable personality of the dead, mankind has addressed itself to this object throughout the ages. And its efforts have always illustrated the twin themes of pity and fear. The hunter warrior must have his weapons and his dogs with him in the grave, the head of the house his servants and his wives, and both their finery and their food. So they would be happy and at ease and the bereaved could feel a little comforted; and if they were happy and at ease perhaps they would not come back.

When the dead man is a great man, another theme is added revealing motives with the same rich human mixture of the noble and the base. The qualities of the hero are worshipped, are desired, and are pursued with devotion and without scruple. Primitive man seems very early to have thought the most obvious way to assimilate the virtues of the hero was to assimilate his body, actually to eat his flesh in the expectation that the spirit which had animated it would also be conveyed and absorbed—a robuster conception of organotherapy than we have yet come back to. Hence arises the commemorative feast which has penetrated Western civilization with what huge significances we know. A second idea which belonged more definitely to the realm of magic was to make an image of the hero, and so preserve his personality without limit; thus the qualities most desired could be judiciously magnified, and above all the whole conception was under control.

But the primitive mind with its dangerous gift of logic could not leave the subject without a further rational expansion. If heroic virtues are transferable at death, must one wait upon the operation of mere natural processes? We need not doubt that the plain conclusion has

been on due occasion reached. When the slayer was
assured of acquiring the virtues of the slain, the crazy
logic of memorial piety had reached its climax. This
dark theme wanders elusively in the customs and folk-
lore of early man, and has its classical seat where in the
shadowy southern woods we discern the enigmatic figure
of the Priest of Nemi with the Golden Bough.

It would be easy to fall into absurdity by making
crude and over-simplified applications of these primitive
modes of thought to our modern affairs. Nevertheless
we must not forget the ingrained conservatism of
Nature; physiology has shown to how large an extent
the fundamental chemistry of the body and the elementary working of the nervous system tend to be uniform
throughout the animal world.[1] There is good reason to
suppose that the same kind of elementary uniformity
obtains and has always obtained in the reactions of men's
minds. If the ideas we have indicated occurred in primitive minds we may be sure that manifest or latent evi-
dences of them will be found in our own. At any rate
we cannot deny that the commemorative feast has its
part in modern memorial celebrations; or that man still
likes to make images of his heroes—though there may
be little enough magic about some of them—and to
magnify the features he thinks they ought to have, and
suppress the others.

It would partake too much of the nature of the over-
strained ingenuity I have already deprecated, to enlarge
upon the traces of what we may call the Golden Bough
theme that are to be found in the treatment by society
of its men of exceptional character and capacity. Such
traces are to be met with, but they are perhaps too

[1] Hopkins, Sir F. Gowland: Anniversary Address, *Proc. Roy. Soc.*, Jan.
1932, p. 420.

elusive to be put into words without an effect of crudity
and exaggeration.

V

The *conscious* and *ostensible* motives under whose influence we approach the commemoration of great men
are first, to contemplate in humble piety and emulation
a largeness of mind and character that far exceeds our
own, and secondly, to seek inspiration from struggles
heroically engaged and perhaps triumphantly won.
There is no commoner mistake in practical psychology
than to suppose that because a motive is admirable it
must therefore be strong. If we are to be honest with
ourselves we shall have to admit that aspirations such
as these do not accompany us very far along the hum-
drum and ignoble ways of daily life. Many of us must
have felt guiltily conscious of how little the exhilaration
produced by such exercises has been able to compete
with the anxieties and ambitions of our own pedestrian
lives. Side by side with this weakness in our conscious
motives, there is, as I have hinted, reason to suspect the
presence of other and submerged impulses, the vestiges
of a cruder, harsher type of feeling, which for all their
dimness may have a certain ugly strength. When we
remember in addition the difficulty of establishing and
keeping alive the true and unadulterated personality of
the dead, we must, I think, confess that the art of ceremonial commemoration has to overcome obstacles of a
very formidable kind if it is to avoid becoming increasingly formalized and superficial.

It is possible that a future and more realistic age may
reach the conclusion that the time to celebrate its heroes
is while they are alive, and not to wait with our remarkable patience until they are safely dead. Such an age

will perhaps reason in its clear way that its duty towards its great men is to get as much out of them as it can, and that no piety after their death can equal in effectiveness for the purpose a receptive and sympathetic understanding during their lives.

VI

It is unfortunately very much easier to recognize a man's greatness after he is dead and when we are freed from the distraction of the actual presence which unhappily tends so often to be odd, angular, and even quarrelsome. It is also an old story that the reception of new ideas tends always to be grudging or hostile. The text is a favourite one and is apt to become the theme of exhortations which, in addition to having the dreariness of their kind, are pointless because they constitute a frontal attack on an ingrained quality of the mind.

Apart from the happy few whose work has already great prestige or lies in fields that are being actively expanded at the moment, discoverers of new truths always find their ideas resisted. The consideration of this process is often obscured by two assumptions: first it is supposed that the most harmful resistance comes from obvious and noisy prejudice and that the more dangerous resistance of inertia and quasi-rational negation is unimportant; and secondly, it is supposed that workers in science are of course free from any resistive tendency but a rational conservatism. Each of these assumptions is an almost complete delusion.

The vociferous opposition met with by the ideas of Charles Darwin and of Lister probably did nothing to hinder the spread of these, and probably brought them within reach of a larger number of people capable of accepting them than would have been the case if the

opposition had been well behaved. Again it was not noisy prejudice that caused the work of Mendel to lie dead for thirty years, but the sheer inability of contemporary opinion to distinguish between a new idea and nonsense. That this same inability may be shown even by the most eminent workers in science scarcely needs demonstration for anyone at all aware of the history of knowledge, but it may be illustrated by an anecdote which we owe to the third Lord Rayleigh and which is to be found in the delightful *Life*[1] of that very great and wise man. J. J. Waterston was an engineer who interested himself in mathematical physics, and in 1845 wrote a paper on the molecular theory of gases which was ten or fifteen years in advance of his time and anticipated much of the work of physicists no less eminent than Joule, Clausius, and even Clerk Maxwell. The only contemporary judgement on this paper that survives is that of the referee of the Royal Society to whom it was submitted. He said, 'The paper is nothing but nonsense'. What Waterston might have accomplished if he had had the recognition and encouragement upon which this genius seems to have been unusually dependent, is beyond conjecture. He did not get them. His work lay in utter oblivion for forty-five years until it was exhumed by the pious efforts of Rayleigh. He himself lived on disappointed and obscure for many years, and then was overtaken by a yet deeper obscurity, for as the result of some strange accident or a long gathering impulse of despair, he disappeared and left no sign.

This little story must strike with a chill upon anyone impatient for the advance of knowledge, and especially upon such as are inclined to assume the use of the scientific method to be synonymous with the possession of the

[1] *Life of Lord Rayleigh.* London, 1924, p. 169 et seq.

scientific mind. Experience fully proves that this assumption is unsound, for there is no limit to the narrowness of the field within which the scientific method may be limited while the rest of the mind is uninfluenced. Even if that assumption is not maintained, there are several grounds on which has been defended the proposition that a man of science does well not to traffic very freely with new ideas. It is thought that the necessary concentration on a limited problem is apt to be attenuated by the use of any general intellectual activity. A proposition more worthy of serious attention is that which declares that scepticism and suspended judgement are the very essence of the scientific mind and scarcely to be depended on too much. The conception is no doubt true when its elements are exactly defined. Without such definition these venerable phrases may very easily become mere snares; this is because they are apt to be the expression not of the principles they profess to represent but of far more deeply ingrained and potent impulses.

The mind delights in a static environment, and if there is any change to be itself the source of it. Change from without, interfering as it must with the sovereignty of the individual, seems in its very essence to be repulsive and an object of fear. A little self-examination tells us pretty easily how deeply rooted in the mind is the fear of the new, and how simple it is when fear is afoot to block the path of the new idea by unbelief and call it scepticism, and by misunderstanding and call it suspended judgement. The only way to the serene sanity which is the scientific mind—but how difficult consistently to follow—is to give to every fresh idea its one intense moment of cool but imaginative attention before venturing to mark it for rejection or suspense, as alas nine times out of ten we must do. In this traffic it is

above all necessary not to be heavy-handed with ideas. It is the function of notions in science to be useful, to be interesting, to be verifiable, and to acquire value from *any one* of these qualities. Scientific notions have little to gain as science from being forced into relation with that formidable abstraction 'general truth'. Any such relation is only too apt to discourage the getting rid of the superseded and the absorption of the new which make up the very metabolism of the mind.

VII

In making this small survey of the simpler reflections that are suggested by commemorative occasions such as this, three general conceptions have presented themselves rather prominently. Some of them at least have a practical bearing and we should therefore be very unworthy disciples of the Master we celebrate if we did not give them what point we can by a particular reference.

The first of these ideas is the familiar truth that if any human institution is looked into at all closely it is found, however admirable its ostensible purpose, to be built out of a strange mixture of elements and to comprise motives many of them odd and some of them ugly. Memorial ceremonies show themselves to be of this class, and thereby demonstrate that they possess a thoroughly natural origin. In these mild disclosures there is nothing to dismay, and no one need be disconcerted by the homely skeletons in the cupboards of folk-lore. At the same time they perhaps have a use in explaining why the stimulation and enlargement of mind afforded by such commemorations are sometimes less potent than we could wish.

The second conception that emerges is the suggestion

that with the process of time it will become increasingly difficult to separate the commemoration of the dead from the responsibility for their treatment during life, or to believe that posthumous honour is in any real sense a reparation for the dead, or a discharge of the liability of the living. It will become less and less possible to regard the discoverer of truth as responsible for the propagation of it, and charged with the duty of converting a stiff-necked generation.

The third and last idea on which our discussion has converged is that if mankind is to profit freely from the small and sporadic crop of the heroically gifted it produces, it will have to cultivate the delicate art of handling ideas. Psychology is now able to tell us with reasonable assurance that the most influential obstacle to freedom of thought and to new ideas is fear; and fear which can with inimitable art disguise itself as caution or sanity or reasoned scepticism or on occasion even as courage.

We may now attempt for a final moment to link these speculations with our primary theme. In his mental environment Hunter must be regarded as a happy man. He lived in the relative intellectual freedom of the best part of the eighteenth century, before its bland sunshine had died in the smoke of industrialism, and before the French Revolution and the reaction to it had deadened speculative thought. He saw, as from a peak in Darien, the illimitable ocean of biology before him and he addressed himself unhesitatingly to explore it all. It was in the general level of knowledge and in instrumental equipment that he was less fortunate. When a new Hunter appears he will not be held back by an undeveloped science and he will find this College able to give him all the facilities with which it has been

munificently endowed. Let us hope that he will also find
an intellectual environment where even his most revolutionary ideas will be planted in a nourishing soil and
bathed in a genial air.

A LANDMARK IN MODERN NEUROLOGY[1]

I

THERE is perhaps no custom which we accept as a matter of course more readily than the ceremonial commemoration of past events. The facility with which exercises of this kind are set going indeed suggests the suspicion that they are animated by motives both numerous and mixed; and we may well remember in confirmation the strange and even scandalous allegations of psychology about the things that lie behind our most ordinary conduct. Happily it is neither my task nor my wish to touch on such obscurities, or to try to sound the molten subterranean magma on which the continents of virtuous behaviour so blandly float. Even the suspicion, however, that motives may not always be as they seem, lays upon us the duty to define quite clearly what we propose should be our attitude of mind in approaching an occasion such as this. If we succeed we shall, moreover, obtain the secondary advantage of some security against the lapses of proportion and of emphasis, which the spirit of celebration may be a little inclined to indulge.

I yield to the temptation that besets the maker of definitions, and begin with some of the elements the commemorative impulse should control or reject. In the first place we do well to deny ourselves any strong tincture of that antiquarian spirit which delights to note in the doings of our forbears the qualities of the merely old-world and quaint. In the second place we shall do

---

[1] An Address delivered at the house of the Royal Society of Medicine on 27 Nov. in commemoration of Sir Rickman Godlee's pioneer operation performed at the Hospital for Epilepsy and Paralysis on 25 Nov. 1884. Reprinted from the *Lancet*, 1 Dec. 1934, p. 1207.

well to use a reasonable proportion and measure on our laudation of departed greatness. The pious exercise of praising famous men is no doubt a highly respectable if rather sedentary occupation. I would not be supposed to deprecate it, but I venture the reminders that praise in its higher flights is apt to get at odds with understanding and that even the truthful Samuel Johnson did not require a man to be on his oath in an epitaph. These reserves are no longer necessary when we direct our commemorative zeal towards the pursuit of reality. The vividness and the immediacy of contemporary events are apt to conceal from us how little of their full quality and outline we are able to discern. It is only the past event that can be seen as part of the pattern of things and with an approach to substantial reality. On an occasion such as this, then, we shall best serve our object if we take advantage of the distance of the event to examine it in its general relations and the light of its secular context, and throughout in the spirit of a strict realism.

II

We are to recall a surgical operation that was done at the Hospital for Epilepsy and Paralysis on 25 November 1884—fifty years ago and well within the reach of living memory. The insidious action of memory must not, however, be allowed to obscure the fact that in going back to that time it leaps a gulf between us and another age. We shall not get a proportioned view of our event unless we pause a moment to call up the world in which it took place. In 1884 we find ourselves in the richest depths of the Victorian era, and the warm tranquil air of its impenetrable security closes round us. The stability and permanence of the scene are embodied in the everlastingness of the three world-figures which

dominate it—Queen Victoria, Gladstone, Bismarck—
figures which seemed so extravagantly different then
but which disclose a certain similarity to-day. An ultimate and real security enclosed the body and spirit. The
land belonged to its monarchs, the seas belonged to
England, and the firmament was unconquered though
perhaps still a little vaguely claimed by the Church. In
science the air was as yet unadulterated with inert gases,
and matter still sat contentedly in its little hard globular
and indestructible atoms. The British Empire was still
without self-consciousness and without a voice, though
a couple of years later it was to find both as the whole
epoch swung to its zenith in the Jubilee of 1887. Ten
years still further on the Jubilee of 1897 would find the
voice of Empire already a little strident and uneasy, the
light perceptibly that of evening and the shadows lying
long on the ground. But the golden decade of the
eighties seems in memory bathed in the timeless light
of summer afternoons into whose tranquillity no storm
could conceivably break.

This is not to say that there were no occasional
rumblings on the horizon which seemed to indicate that
some day the weather might change. While the group
of doctors to whose doings we are presently to come
had done their operation, and were watching their
patient with declining hopes through anxious weeks,
General Gordon, hopelessly shut up in Khartoum, was
watching the approach of a doom as inevitable as that
of the sick man, whom he was only just to outlive.

III

So much for the general context in which the event
we are to celebrate had its course. Its special context
will concern us more when we have recalled the event

itself. The story of the case has been retold quite lately by Sir D'Arcy Power in the vivid way we all know, and I therefore need provide no more than a curt summary of the facts in the modern rather than the contemporary idiom. The patient was a man of 25 with no other evidence of abnormality than his cerebral symptoms. For three years he had shown slowly progressive evidence of a lesion in or near the central cortex of the right hemisphere. The succession of symptoms showed typical Jacksonian attacks with occasional loss of consciousness. The limited attacks were first in the left side of the face and tongue and then in the left hand and arm. For about six months there had been weakness of the left arm and for three months before the time of admission to the hospital on 3 November the patient had had to give up work because the left arm was useless. From the time of admission there had been slight weakness of the left leg, and severe pressure symptoms had set in, namely intense paroxysmal headache and vomiting, and well-marked papilloedema with haemorrhages. The diagnosis was made of a tumour 'probably of limited size involving the cortex of the brain and situated at the middle part of the fissure of Rolando'. This conclusion was put before the patient who was intelligent enough to understand, and brave enough to accept the course proposed by the doctors. On 25 November the tumour was found and removed by operation through an opening immediately over and but little larger than the tumour itself. Only one cerebral convolution was exposed—the ascending parietal as was afterwards proved—it was slightly yellow and relatively avascular. When it was incised a tumour was disclosed at the depth of $\frac{1}{8}$ inch. This showed an apparent encapsulation, but was enucleated piecemeal and subsequently described as a glioma.

The immediate effect of the operation was wholly satisfactory. There was a slight increase of the hemiplegic weakness but all the other symptoms were relieved and the intelligence was fully retained. It had been proved for the first time that without the least external abnormality of the skull to point the way, a focal lesion of the brain substance could be found and could be removed by operation leaving the general functions of the brain unimpaired.

Complete success, success such as would have been palpable even to the 'world's coarse thumb and finger', was denied these valiant men. A slow infection of the wound occurred, and after four miserable weeks of disappointed hopes the patient died of meningitis. It would be beyond the limits of my task to comment on this operation from the point of view of the modern surgery of the brain of which it is one of the cornerstones. The remark may, however, be made that if these pioneers were unfortunate in their efforts to exclude infection, they were fortunate in having as their first case one in which the neurological and anatomical localization of the lesion could be made so brilliantly exact.

IV

There were present among others at the operation, Hughes Bennett and Godlee, the physician and surgeon directly concerned, and Ferrier and Hughlings Jackson without whose work it would never have been thought of. I do not propose at the moment to say anything more of the two last named. Of Alexander Hughes Bennett I will limit myself to saying that he seems to have been the competent and respectable son of a distinguished father, John Hughes Bennett of Edinburgh. The elder Hughes Bennett, as I cheerfully discard relevance to remind you, introduced the use of cod-liver oil to this country, and tried to persuade the profession to cure rickets eighty years before the discovery of vitamin D. He met with even less success than did James Lind, who tried to persuade the profession to prevent scurvy 150 years before the discovery of vitamin C.

Of Rickman John Godlee the occasion seems to demand an ampler memorial and personal knowledge perhaps to justify the attempt. At the time of the operation we have described he was in his early prime and had been on the staff of University College Hospital for seven years. He was to serve the Hospital for thirty years more with a characteristically punctual assiduity, and a loyalty and judgement that made him one of its mainstays. It is the healthy tradition of the students of that Institution to view their seniors with an unsentimental and not too indulgent eye. I cannot express respect for the memory of Godlee better than by saying that all the influence of his early training and mature judgement, would have approved the attempt to recall him under the guidance of that traditional method, and to see him as he was. He certainly saw us as we were and did not always conceal the result of his observations. His precise, patient, and extraordinarily lucid teaching was invaluable not only for its excellence but also for the conscientious regularity with which it was dispensed, even in his busiest years. He was never harsh but his confidence was difficult to win, and he was an exacting chief who enforced his instructions with a chilly mildness that had its power. I can speak only for one of his pupils, but it took that one a long time to guess at the sensitiveness and personal humility which he defended from the world with a tongue always clever and sometimes a little cruel.

It is scarcely possible to estimate the quality of Godlee as a surgeon without some glance at the men who were his nearest contemporaries on the staff at University College—Arthur Barker his senior by one year, and Horsley his junior by seven years.[1] Each of these two men had the restless curiosity and discontent of the pioneer, each had a strong natural aptitude for operative work, and each in his own field was capable of the highest flights of technical virtuosity. It was natural, therefore, that their interests should tend to be concentrated on special problems, while the rest of surgery was taken very much for granted as common knowledge, though Horsley in particular, when he chose to use it, had an extraordinary flair for all clinical matters. Godlee, on the other hand, was a true and single-minded clinician, for whom the task of the surgeon was to teach and to practise the established doctrines and rules of the art. His attitude to surgery was therefore in the best sense academic and authoritarian, and his work, well controlled by caution and scepticism, had the distinction conferred by a capacious and instructed mind.

It may well seem rather paradoxical that we find a man of this type engaged in the daring adventure that an attack on a cerebral tumour must then have seemed, and I have no doubt that Godlee approached it with at least all the qualms that any conscientious surgeon must have felt. He would be sustained, however, by the knowledge that he possessed two very special qualifications. In the first place, as the nephew of Lister, he could

[1] This group of remarkable men must always be further linked in the memory of the surgical neurologist by the facts that in 1886 Barker was the first in this country to drain successfully an otitic cerebral abscess, and that in 1887 Horsley was the first to remove an accurately localized spinal tumour. The latter achievement was perhaps the least known but not the least substantial contribution to the celebrity of the year that marked the Jubilee of the Queen by whose express wish Horsley had received his first name.

feel able to apply the new antiseptic doctrine in all its purity and might also feel an almost apostolic mission to demonstrate its value in the unknown region of the brain. In the second place, the knowledge that he was a highly competent anatomist must have encouraged him to undertake the difficult task of finding his way to a given convolution guided only by anatomical measurements. It is pleasant to think with what relief and pride the young, conscientious, and perhaps not very self-confident surgeon, must have concluded an operation that has so brilliantly justified every expectation, and so generously rewarded every effort.

No such happy concatenation of circumstances seems to have befallen Godlee again, and throughout his long and extremely distinguished career whatever satisfactions and triumphs he was to enjoy, he was not to experience any more just that special exultation of leading the forlorn hope.

v

In mentioning those who were present on this historic occasion I have said nothing about someone else whose presence even the least sentimental of us must admit to have been indispensable. One's professional mind, perhaps wisely, would prefer to conceal, under the comprehensive label of 'the case', the fact that this person was a human being, and would also prefer to limit any concession of individuality to such remarks as that he was of a good type and that he took the anaesthetic well. With an equally prudent preference for the abstract, the general speaks of his men as 'the troops', and recognizes in them such distant approaches to humanity as that they are smart on parade or steady under fire.

The heresy of admitting that at the centre of this

event there was a human being is possibly condoned by
his short appearance before us not being without a certain tragic dignity. He was young, intelligent, courageous, and he was to die. I owe to the impeccable
memory of a contemporary witness the knowledge that
this young man's name was Henderson and that he was
a native of Dumfries. I record this with pious satisfaction in being able to add a name to the exiguous roll
of those by whose misfortune or endurance the world
has directly gained. It is a strange defect in medical
history to have kept so few of the names of these bene-
factors and to have left it to accident that we still know
there existed such humble but significant people as little
James Phipps and Sarah Nelmes or Alexis St. Martin.
To the high professional spirit treasuring such names
may seem trivial and even a little ludicrous. Let us not
forget, however, that they are the names of those who
have borne more substantial witness than has yet been
produced by any philosopher or any theologian that all
suffering is not in vain.

VI

We have tried, so far, to make some sort of picture
of our event in three ways. First we have touched on the
general environment in which it took place, secondly we
have enumerated some of the happenings of which it
was made up, and thirdly we have given some attention
to the actors who took part in it. It remains to add to the
bare outlines of our necessarily imperfect specification
some comment on the significance, or what I have called
the special context, of the event itself. The first operative removal of a localized cerebral tumour was what
we may call a nodal occurrence that marked the con-
vergence of two distinct processes, the evolution of

operative surgery on the one hand and of neurology on the other.

The development of the remedial use of the knife seems always to have occurred in two stages. In the first, discovery was made that a procedure was anatomically and physiologically feasible and it was applied to what pathological conditions might be hoped to be benefited by it. The essential fact was that the operation could be done at all, and not that it was designed to deal with a given lesion. Thus may have originated most of the classical formal operations—the amputations, the excisions of the tongue and of the jaws which were in essence anatomically conditioned, and without primary orientation towards any disease.

When the anatomical and physiological obstacles to the art have been overcome, and are no longer the surgeon's chief care, it is possible for operations to be orientated specifically towards dealing with a given lesion, and to be designed chiefly in accordance with pathological considerations. Thus we no longer amputate the tongue or excise the jaw or larynx for cancer, we excise the cancer from these regions. Hence the full development of the operative surgery of a part is strictly dependent on its pathology. Though always growing in accordance with this simple principle, the evolution of surgery as a whole was checked and at last almost arrested by the inability to prevent wound infection. In the pre-Listerian ages wound infections were scarcely serious enough to be in themselves a drag on the progress of surgery, so long as the population was thin and scattered. Increase of population and of urbanization went on with progressive rapidity throughout the eighteenth and nineteenth centuries, making unavoidable the aggregation of the sick in hospitals. The inevitable result was that by the middle of the latter period it began to seem doubtful if wound infections would not bring hospital surgery, and with it surgical progress, to a standstill. The result was a highly anomalous situation, in which surgical pathology had got far ahead of surgical treatment. Many conditions were well enough understood pathologically for their treatment to be clear; the anatomical and physiological obstacles to the necessary operation were understood and surmountable; but treatment was impossibly dangerous through the irrelevant factor of wound infections. The Listerian system quickly abolished this anomaly, and there was an immediate harvest of success in conditions of which the pathology was at all reasonably advanced. Where, however, surgical pathology had been able to make little or no substantial progress, then the antiseptic method could gain no immediate results. Progress therefore resumed its normal type, though it was doubtless accelerated by the increased freedom to explore and observe that the surgeon now possessed. Thus though Wölfler did the first gastroenterostomy in 1881 and Koch discovered the tubercle bacillus in 1882, it was near the end of the century before abdominal surgery had fairly assumed its modern aspect, and after the turn of the century before the modern surgery of the thorax began to take form.

The tedium of this digression is justified here, if at all, by the salience it may give to the unique evolution the surgery of the brain has had. It was the good fortune of this branch of the art that at approximately the time when the antiseptic method enlarged, if not indeed created its opportunities, really fundamental discoveries in the physiology and pathology of the brain were being made, so that there was no tendency for operative inventiveness to outrun its pathological foundations.

Progress has been slow through the comparative rarity of its material and the stubborn difficulty that is its everyday characteristic. That slow progress has, however, been steady, and unproductive of the kind of operation, known sometimes in other branches, that flourishes exceedingly and then dies because it has no sound pathological basis.

VII

I have referred to the fundamental discoveries in neurology that did so much to start the surgery of the brain on its course. They will for ever be associated with the work of two men whom we have noted to be present at Godlee's operation—Ferrier and Hughlings Jackson. With some slight reference to that work my task draws to its end.

Whenever we may suppose the idea of a localization of function in the cerebral cortex to have originated, it began to get systematic exploitation with Broca's discovery, in 1861, of a relation between aphasia and lesions of the third left frontal convolution. From that time research followed the two lines of clinical inquiry and animal experimentation. In the clinical field Jackson soon established the position of a master and within a few years had begun the long series of contributions which are among the most precious classics of neurology. The experimental attack began with Fritsch and Hitzig in 1870, who demonstrated the electrical excitability of the anterior part of the cerebrum. Then Ferrier took up the task and in 1873 published a long and detailed paper which carried the subject much farther forward and confirmed in a remarkable way the clinical work of Jackson. The impetus given to the subject by Ferrier was very great, and it was pursued with increasing minuteness and exactitude by physiologist after physiologist. At the time of Godlee's operation, for example, Horsley had already been engaged for nearly a year with Sharpey Schafer at University College on their well-known work on the monkey's brain. These bare references are enough to recall the atmosphere of vigorous neurological expansion of the period with which we are concerned. In some ways also they perhaps make it seem more remote. I cannot deny myself a reminder that tends against this last impression. Ferrier's classical paper was published in the Medical Report of the West Riding Lunatic Asylum for 1873. I almost feel I should digress to apologize for the crudeness of the name which the then backward state of psychiatry allowed this institution to possess; I wish I could have called it a Mental Hospital, though perhaps the experimental physiology would not have been any better. In this paper, then, Ferrier expresses his thanks to the Medical Director for putting at his disposal the liberal resources of the laboratory in which he had done his work. Sixty-one years later I find myself able in one thing to follow in the footsteps of Ferrier, and that is in expressing my thanks (for help in recording the event we commemorate to-day) to the same distinguished physician, Sir James Crichton Browne.[1]

We have been engaged in recalling one of the victories of the human spirit over chaos. As we take leave of the battle-field we may note that like other famous

---

[1] Sir James Crichton Browne has been good enough to inform me that though not actually present at Godlee's operation he was acquainted with the case both before and after and was well qualified through his familiarity with the patient's native place to test his memory after the operation. Sir James was the author of the well-known letter in *The Times* signed 'F.R.S.' which pointed out the direct dependence of the operation on the results of animal experiment, and which led to some controversy and also to two valuable leading articles in that journal.

victories its results have not altogether been the expected. It was fought in the strength of three great principles—the antiseptic system with all its chemical lotions and its sprays, the precise projection of the cerebral markings on the surface of the skull as a preliminary to operation, and the doctrine of the exact localization of cortical function. The first two have long been abandoned by the surgeon and I should be sorry to have to define the present position of the third. Nevertheless each has left a substantial legacy of which the invigorating influence in surgical neurology remains perennial. Thus though we might hesitate to fight a similar battle to-day under the guidance of these time-worn champions, we can yet believe that the event they directed was a real event, and one worthy of our respectful commemoration.

THE INSULATION OF THE NERVOUS SYSTEM[1]

WITHIN a few days it will be exactly ten years since Victor Horsley died. The circumstances of his death, however lamentable they may seem to us who lost him, were not, perhaps, very different from what he himself might have wished. He was at work in the direct service of his country, he was using his whole strength in the relief of suffering, while his mind and body kept unabated their astonishing and characteristic vigour. In commemorating this great man our attention is attracted to three separate aspects of his life. We think of him as a physiologist and as a surgical pioneer, and we think of the personality which lay behind and informed these and all the activities of his crowded years.

His work for science and for surgery has long been incorporated with the general body of knowledge and has its lasting place. For his personality there is no such lodgement, and those in whose memory it lives so vividly are already, after the passage of even ten years, a heavily reduced company. I therefore gratefully accept this chance to make my small record of a man who in my knowledge of men was unique in this—that he combined an inflexible belief in his own standards and a truly apostolic zeal in all public affairs, with a disposition that was in its essence boyish and simple and in every private relation easy and mild and kind.

METHODS OF INVESTIGATION IN NEUROLOGY

The pioneer work of Horsley in the surgery of the central nervous system has had and must continue to

---

[1] The second Victor Horsley Memorial Lecture, delivered at the House of the British Medical Association on Friday, 9 July. Reprinted from the *British Medical Journal*, 17 July 1926.

have important remote and secondary effects upon the development of neurology. Whenever a region of the body has been made accessible to surgery, a new insight into its pathology has resulted from the fresh experience that has been acquired of morbid processes in the living and especially of the earlier stages of disease. This has been abundantly shown in the case of the abdomen and in the case of the thorax. In that of the central nervous system it is perhaps as yet less obvious, but it is already unmistakable and will become increasingly so as experience accumulates.

While most of us would no doubt agree that important practical knowledge is to be acquired in this way, there are probably few who look to it with much hope for the discovery of principles of general scope and fundamental significance. As a possible source of any wide expansion of neurological theory it is just and natural to look to laboratory methods and the study of animals rather than to methods of the bedside and to the study of man himself in his reactions to injury and disease. In the familiar and not always philosophically made comparison between the experimental and clinical methods it is usually, however, overlooked that the latter has of necessity a virtue which is in some degree its special possession. The student whose material is man is drastically handicapped by the limited extent to which experiment is open to him. He must take his problems as he finds them, and deny himself the help of almost all the preliminary simplifications which are the essence of the laboratory worker's advantage. At the same time, however, the conditions of his work impose upon him a knowledge of his material at once so intimate and so wide as to constitute a situation probably unique in the whole field of science. When we consider the intensity of watchfulness which the quite ordinary practice of neural surgery calls for and obtains, it must be obvious that the behaviour of the human brain in the various circumstances of injury and disease is far better known than that of any other animal. Indeed, one of the characteristic difficulties of the clinician comes from this very abundance of the stuff of observation, and he is likely to be overwhelmed by its bulk and rendered inattentive by its familiarity, losing amongst details his sense for larger groupings, and amidst the everyday his eye for the significant. Nevertheless the history of science shows that one important source of general ideas has been just this very circumstance of a close intimacy with a large range of observed facts.

The familiarity with the behaviour of the central nervous system that has been possible since it has been accessible to surgical exploration and treatment is capable of reacting in an important way on our attitude to neurological theory.

The Abstract Method in Neurology

There are few departments in biological science in which what we may call abstract methods of thought are more naturally and inevitably used than they are in neurology. By abstract methods I mean methods in which the single or grouped items of experience are for convenience of thought represented by abstracted summaries of themselves or symbols, which have a handiness for working on in the mind that the raw undigested facts cannot possess. The discovery of the uses of abstraction was an event of fundamental importance in the evolution of science, and in the early Greek natural philosophers we can see with what exultation was welcomed the extension it gave to the powers of the mind. Perfectly legitimate and indeed indispensable as the method is, it is obviously not applicable to all material of inquiry with equal ease and safety. With what certainty and precision the qualities of number, space, and motion allow of abstraction is seen in the noble achievements of mathematics, physics, and astronomy—achievements which, through their most recent extensions in atomic and in stellar physics, have finally established the overwhelming prestige of the method and its effective leadership in science.

When, however, we make living matter and living organisms the subject of study we find that though we can by no means dispense with the use of abstraction it is far less effective in application and has disadvantages which it does not seem to possess in the inorganic world. In biological inquiry an abstract conception, though professedly no more than a convenient summary of experience and constantly subject to the censorship of facts, is apt to acquire a quasi-vitality of its own through which it loses its immediate dependence on experience and comes to dominate instead of serving. The danger arises not so much from the extreme cases of conceptions which easily show as flagrantly inconsistent with facts, but from ideas primarily good and sound which have been endowed with a prestige that in their very nature they could not deserve. That an overvaluation of the abstract conception as an implement of research can deceive even the very elect could be shown by many eminent examples. The biological writings of Herbert Spencer are perhaps as good an instance as comes readily to mind, and it is easy to trace in them how this very weakness has led within a few years to their greatly diminished influence. To find so distinguished a man in a state of reprobation may well make humble people look anxiously to their own doctrines; and indeed which of us, for example, can ask himself without a qualm what is the *exact* meaning he attaches to the abstract conception of evolution which has dominated the biological world for half a century?

When we turn to neurology we find the currency and influence of abstract conceptions very great—as, for example, in the theory of aphasia, in Hughlings Jackson's interpretation of cerebral functions, in Monakow's doctrine of diaschisis, and so forth. All these are doubtless, in their essence and originally, good and valuable conceptions; it is another matter, however, how far their function as professed summaries of experience is kept distinct from their charm as mere intellectual patterns. It is thus peculiarly necessary for neurology to submit itself to the discipline of frequent returns to the comparatively primitive and clumsy method of direct and concrete thinking. Such efforts should, I think, be guided by two principles. The first is the obvious one that a constant and docile reference to experience is indispensable. The second is perhaps less obvious and is less simple to state; it accepts the free use of hypothesis as essential to neurological progress, but it enjoins that in drawing up our necessarily more or less abstract conceptions of the nature and working of the nervous system we should incline to the use of ideas of a definitely biological type, and should as far as possible avoid concepts that in their very nature can have no direct resemblance to what actually happens in the body. In giving to our neurological ideas this concrete and realistic tone we shall always depend to a great extent on an intimate familiarity with the appearances and behaviour of the actual nervous tissues. The knowledge of this kind we possess to-day may well be regarded as having in great part grown out of Horsley's work.

The surgical neurologist is perhaps fortunately placed for considering the nervous system in an attitude of mind at once general and concrete; while he lacks the special knowledge of the anatomist, the physiologist, and the pathologist, he is also free from their special preoccupations; while the behaviour of the nervous tissues in injury and disease is a matter of familiar knowledge, it is prevented from becoming commonplace by the narrow margin of safety within which he works and the serious consequences that follow when it is exceeded. Thus is almost forced on him the development of views which, whatever they may lack in the way of abstruse detail, will at any rate always tend to be strictly realistic.

Injuries to the Limiting Structures of the Nervous System

In illustration of this general point of view I propose to call attention to a small group of facts which while they are of more or less common knowledge are perhaps more especially within the observation of the surgeon. They are concerned with the responses of the nervous system to certain injuries.

Division of a Nerve

It is a very old observation that when a mixed peripheral nerve is cut its central end becomes swollen into a bulbous mass of dense fibrous tissue. It seems sometimes to be thought that this is only an occasional result of a nerve section and is especially to be looked for when persistent pain has followed the injury. This is, of course, not the fact. The bulbous end is the invariable and inevitable result of a nerve section to which it is the necessary and so to say physiological response. When we inquire into the exact nature of this so-called amputation neuroma we find that in immediate consequence of the section the nerve fibres ramify and grow out from the cut end so that there issues from this a veritable spray of fine naked axis cylinders. The result of this invasion is to call forth an energetic response from the adjacent non-neural tissue leading to the formation of a peculiarly dense fibrous material that resists the spread of the nerve fibrils and finally encloses them in an impenetrable capsule. Within this limiting substance the growth of axis cylinders continues, but since there is no exit it can result only in the formation of an intricate and aimlessly convoluted network.

Breaches of the Spinal Theca

It occasionally happens, usually perhaps in connexion with the avulsion of a spinal nerve, that a subcutaneous laceration of the spinal dura occurs. More commonly the surgeon has an opportunity of studying the effect of breaches of the theca in cases where a laminectomy with incision of the membranes has to be followed by a second similar operation after some weeks or months. We find then that wherever the cerebrospinal fluid has been able to escape into the tissues it has been everywhere walled off by a dense impervious membrane, so that, according to the extent to which the fluid has made its way, there will be a more or less complicated series of cyst-like spaces communicating with the intrathecal cavity. It is the wall of these cystic extensions of the theca that is of interest, for it shows all the characters of the normal dura. It is of a dense, fibrous substance, its inner surface is smooth and glistening, and its outer surface, instead of merging with the surrounding tissues like a scar, is easily separable from them along a well marked line of cleavage.

Regeneration of the Cerebral Dura

It is not uncommon for a second cerebral operation to be necessary in a case in which the dura mater has already been opened or removed. If the second operation is done after an interval of about six weeks or more it will be found that the gap, however large, that was left in the dura at the first operation has been closed by the formation of a new membrane having all the characters of normal dura as above described. Among such characters the most striking, and perhaps the most conclusive of the nature of the new membrane, is its differentiation from the overlying scalp, so that the latter can be stripped away from it with ease and without bleeding. It is interesting to note that at one time a great deal of surgical ingenuity was expended on evolving a plastic surgery of the dura, in which gaps were closed by the insertion of fascial grafts. Such grafts were always remarkably successful because a new dura would have formed quite naturally and equally well without them.

Here we have a group of three well-defined facts established by countless observations and capable of confirmation at any time. They bring evidence from different parts of the nervous system disclosing even to superficial consideration a clear common tendency. The conclusion to which all point is that breaches of the normal coverings of the nervous tissues allowing contact between the latter and other tissues of the body result of necessity in energetic local reactions. The obvious function of such reactive processes is to reestablish the normal discontinuity between neural and somatic tissues and to break the contact that has caused the disturbance.

We have met, then, with a mechanism of a definitely physiological type which may well prove to be concerned with the very nature of the nervous system. Our next inquiry will naturally be, What is the immediate agent of the reaction we are concerned with? In the case of the divided nerve it seems clear that the escaping naked axis cylinder is the actual irritant substance; in the case of the spinal theca it is evident that the cerebrospinal fluid is the effective agent; in the case of the cerebral dura it is probable that in ordinary conditions with an intact arachnoid, fluid exuding through this is the excitant, though the contact of the brain itself is doubtless also effective. It is seen, then, that there is a common property possessed by naked nerve-fibres, by cerebrospinal fluid, and almost certainly by the brain substance itself, which enables these to set up in the somatic tissues an energetic reaction the tendency of which is to insulate the one from the other. There is evidence that the neural side of the contact, while effective as an irritant, does not contribute to the newly formed tissue which, whether in the form of the fibromatous material of the bulbous nerve or in that of the extemporized dura, is of purely non-neural origin though obviously a highly specialized material and no mere scar.

FUNCTIONAL EFFECTS OF BREACHES IN INSULATION

When we see such well defined mechanisms for the sealing of breaches in neural insulation we naturally should expect to find such breaches to be of great functional importance and capable of causing serious disturbance in the tissues unnaturally brought into contact. There is in fact evidence that some effect on function is produced, but it is not to the mere prevention of this that we can look to explain the actual existence of these mechanisms themselves; that seems to depend, as we shall see, on some far more fundamental causation. The chief evidence of disturbed function is seen in the case of the divided nerve. Here there are symptoms suggesting persistent excitation of the cut end. These are always present from the first, but they vary greatly in intensity. The sensation of the presence of the limb after an amputation is universal, and it always lasts for several weeks. Not uncommonly it is painful, and then it tends to be more persistent and may last for years. The facts suggest that the exposed nerve fibres of the stump are excited by contact with the tissues, and that in the bulbous end the stimulation effect gradually dies down until a state of equilibrium is established in which the new tissue sealing off the nerve end is practically as inert towards the nerve as is its normal sheath.

It is natural to suppose that after a wound of the brain which allowed a scar of non-neural origin to come into close contact with the brain substance a state of excitation might be set up. The frequency of traumatic epilepsy in cases of direct scarring of the brain is perhaps suggestive, but I know of no evidence that allows us to take the case beyond a mere suspicion.

On the somatic side of a breach of neural insulation there is no disturbance of function beyond the mere reaction already described. It is, indeed, characteristic of this that it is always and only strictly local. There is nothing in the way even of a diffuse or spreading fibrosis; the new tissue, whether it be an amputation neuroma or a new segment of dura, and although it is of somatic origin, becomes sharply differentiated from the tissues it is derived from, and can be separated from them easily without cutting, We see, therefore, that although breaches of neural insulation are immediately dealt with by energetic, effective, and highly specialized mechanisms, the actual disturbances of function produced by such breaches do not seem to be very important.

INSULATORY ARRANGEMENTS IN THE NORMAL NERVOUS SYSTEM

If the evidence I have cited bears the meaning I have given it and we can regard as of high importance to the body the maintenance of neural insulation, then we can look for confirmation in normal structure and expect to find dispositions in relation to the nervous system which are insulatory in function. From the nature of the reaction we have seen to be set up by breaches of insulation we may infer that the influence against which insulatory mechanisms are provided is chemical in kind, and this inference may serve as a guiding principle in the search.

Insulation of the Peripheral Nerves

Beginning our survey with the peripheral nerves we may at once dismiss from consideration the medullary sheath, which, whatever its physical insulatory function may be, is clearly not in question as a chemical insulant, since non-medullated nerves lie as peacefully and as inert in the tissues as the medullated. The case is different, however, with the neurilemma. Here we have a sheath common to all nerves outside the central axis, and continuous without a break from spinal cord or brain to end-organ. The motor nerve fibre is clothed from within the central nervous system to the muscle fibre, where the neurilemma completes the sealing off of unnatural contacts by becoming continuous with the sarcolemma itself. The sensory fibres are similarly clothed throughout their

length; at their peripheral termination they enter end-
organs all of which throughout a great variety of structure show—with one suggestive exception—so marked
an encapsulatory arrangement that one cannot but think
that here the need for insulation must be especially vital.
The one sensory nerve fibre which is known to terminate
in an end-organ which is not of a strongly capsular type
is the fibre that serves the sense of pain. This fibre ends
in a free arborization in the tissue to which it is distributed, and this terminal part is uncovered by neurilemma. It cannot but strike us as significant, though I
shall not take up the point further at the moment, that
this anomaly of a sensory fibre making naked contact
with the somatic tissues should be a character of the fibre
concerned with pain, a form of sensibility that in itself
is so profoundly anomalous.

The view that the neurilemma is the chemically insulating structure we are looking for is confirmed by the
fact that within the central nervous system, where insulation is otherwise provided, it is defective or altogether
absent. A point further suggestive of the importance of
insulation in the peripheral nerves is the evidence we
have that there is an upward drainage along their trunks,
so that the products of their metabolism are probably
kept from contact with surrounding tissues and are conveyed into the central theca.

Insulation of the Central Nervous System

When we turn to the central nervous system we find
that the method of individual insulation no longer pre-
vails, but that the whole mass of the central axis is pro-
tected as one unit. Plainly, of course, it is the meninges
which are chiefly concerned. Of these we have already
seen that the dura has so important a function that acci-

dental defects in it are repaired with very remarkable rapidity and completeness. The *mechanically protective* function of the dura, which doubtless has its importance, can scarcely be regarded as explaining its peculiarly impervious texture, its double endothelial surface, and the marked line of cleavage that separates it even when newly formed from the surrounding tissues. All these, however, acquire meaning when they are regarded as evidence of its *chemically insulatory* capacity. Effective as the dura doubtless is in its way, it deals only with one relatively small part of the problem of insulation. If we are right in supposing that all neuro-somatic contacts are inadmissible and that the blood and blood-vessels belong to the somatic side of the frontier, the nutrition of so large a bulk of nervous tissue as the central nervous system must involve dispositions altogether unique in the body, and we should expect, in regarding the circulatory mechanisms of the part from this point of view, to meet with features of a very special kind.

The cerebrospinal fluid and its circulation, the existence and disposition of the multiple membranes of the brain, and the absence of a recognizable lymphatic system in the ordinary sense of the term, constitute a picture which is unique, and has admittedly defied thorough explanation. Let us consider it in relation to the avoidance of undue contact between neural and non-neural elements.

THE CEREBROSPINAL FLUID

Let me briefly review the strange facts of the physiology of the cerebrospinal fluid as they are now known. The cerebrospinal fluid is an extremely dilute secretion profusely poured out by the choroid plexuses of the cerebral ventricles. It flows through the central cavities of the brain and issues therefrom through the roof of the fourth ventricle into the subarachnoid space. Through this so-called space, which has rather the structure of a cellular spongework, it courses partly into the spinal canal, but chiefly upwards and forwards over the brain, to escape into the venous circulation through the arachnoid villi that project into the various lateral extensions of the superior longitudinal sinus. As is well known, any obstruction to the flow in any part of this intricate course downwards within the brain and upwards outside of it inevitably leads to an accumulation of the fluid and to hydrocephalus. Such obstructions are easily produced and common.

The cerebrospinal fluid with its circulation, whatever function it may be there to perform, shows itself, then, to constitute a weak spot in the cerebral organization that as it were invites pathological attack. That the cerebral apparatus should contain an arrangement in some ways so seriously disadvantageous, suggests that the mechanism must have some deep functional significance that is indispensable to the physiology of the body.

There is no lymphatic system in the ordinary sense in the brain or spinal cord, and no flow outwards through the cerebrospinal envelopes of anything corresponding with lymph occurs anywhere. It seems clear that products of nervous metabolism find their way into the cerebrospinal fluid in the subarachnoid space; there is, in fact, strong clinical evidence that this fluid has a definite toxicity for the rest of the body, for when it is liberated into the tissues high fever is apt to occur during the short period before absorption is arrested by the inevitable reaction in the tissues that produces encystment. It is thought that metabolic products reach the cerebrospinal fluid along the so-called perivascular lymphatics. These remarkable structures are tubular extensions of the subarachnoid space which accompany and enclose the vessels that penetrate the brain to their finest ramifications. The interpretation of their meaning has long been regarded as a great difficulty, but if we accept the view that somatic structures like the blood-vessels cannot be admitted to direct contact with the nervous tissues it is natural to regard the perivascular lymphatics as mechanisms to insulate the blood-vessels from this contact. It may be assumed from what we know of the nourishment of tissues in general that there is some kind of leakage from the cerebral tissues comparable with lymph as found everywhere else and presumably of a not dissimilar concentration. This fluid will find its way to the subarachnoid space, presumably by the perivascular channels. The disposal of such a material may well be regarded as an exacting task. It is impregnated with products of nerve metabolism and is an eminently 'neural' fluid capable of producing energetic reactions in any somatic tissue it meets. Thus there can be no question of its entering the blood-stream in the relatively high concentrations that are satisfactory for lymph, and Nature meets the case by providing for its being heavily diluted before it is allowed to join the somatic blood in the cranial sinuses.

The most characteristic feature of the cerebrospinal fluid as it exudes from the choroid plexuses is its remarkably low solid content. It is by far the most watery secretion produced by the normal body, and one might almost say it is an attempt by Nature to secrete pure water. It contains a small amount of the diffusible substances of the blood, but practically nothing else. So strong is the tendency to keep the fluid watery that the choroid plexuses have a truly astonishing impenetrability to drugs and other foreign substances circulating in the blood. Even the bile-pigments in cases of jaundice fail to find a passage. This fluid, practically amounting to nothing but water, is secreted in large quantities; on rare occasions I have had the experience of seeing as the result of accident what was perhaps a large fraction of the total secretion of cerebrospinal fluid discharged on the surface. The amount of fluid escaping has been very large and the consequent inanition correspondingly profound. The normal function of this great flow of water we may suppose with some confidence to be to flush through the whole subarachnoid space and to dilute the products of cerebral metabolism to such a degree that the resulting fluid can be safely admitted to the general blood-stream. This view gets some confirmation from the evidence we have that the fluid in the subarachnoid space has a larger solid content than the fluid in the ventricles.

It is interesting to reflect that the source of this mysterious secretion which has given so much difficulty to the chemical physiologist may turn out to be no more abstruse a thing than Nature's nearest approach in the animal body to a spring of plain water; if this should be so, it may also remind us of the small and amusing coincidence that one part at any rate of the tortuous channel through which the fluid runs—the *aqueduct of Sylvius*—has since the very early days of anatomy borne a singularly exact and appropriate name.

In our review of certain aspects of the nervous system we have found reason to regard as of fundamental importance the preservation of an impenetrable barrier between the whole of the nervous system and the rest of the body. This barrier we have seen to be made up of a number of highly special structures and mechanisms. Its function is on the whole to prevent contact between the neural and the non-neural, but is also in certain places to permit it. These places are only two: first, where the motor nerve end comes into contact with the muscle-fibre, and secondly, where the naked arborization of the pain nerve meets the tissue in which it is distributed. The nervous system is thus kept apart from the body, as we may say, in order that when the two are permitted to meet the reaction shall be the more energetic. It is in fact, then, of the very essence of nervous tissue that it should be different from the other tissues, so that it can irritate and be irritated by them. This necessity for a certain 'strangeness' of the nervous system may possibly throw some light on its curious embryology. The origin of the nervous system, as an epiblastic tube originating on the surface of the body and then sinking into its substance, has been investigated chiefly from the morphological point of view, and great ingenuity and research have been expended on it. It may be worth suggesting, however, that the problem has also a functional side, and that the epiblastic origin of an organ that is ultimately to be deeply embedded in mesoblastic tissues possibly has the function of contributing its strangeness, and therefore its effectiveness, to the nervous system as a whole. This quasi-hostility between neural and somatic, between brain and body, is a suggestive and perhaps a disturbing thought, but we shall not attempt here to follow it out.

Neural Insulation in Pathology

It is more convenient at the moment to consider certain pathological evidence that has some bearing on the conclusions we have already reached.

That the central nervous system differs from other organs in having a certain inaccessibility has long been recognized in connexion with syphilis. The difference between the strictly extraneural mesoblastic infection of the meningeal gumma on the one hand, and the intraneural parenchymatous infection of general paralysis on the other, shows that the frontier between the two regions is as sharply marked pathologically as it is physiologically. Moreover, the relative inefficacy of antisyphilitic treatment in the parenchymatous infection reminds us that the frontier is also impassable for many drugs.

The dura and arachnoid are in some sense intermediate tissues, for they show a certain tolerance for both neural and non-neural contacts, the arachnoid having slightly greater affinities for the former, and the dura perhaps for the latter. That they are, however, fundamentally non-neural in their behaviour, and probably also in their nature, is suggested strongly by their relations to certain tumours. The glioma is probably the one truly neural tumour that affects the central nervous system. Although it behaves within the brain as a malignant infiltrating growth, its spread is restrained by the neuro-somatic barrier, so that while in exceptional cases it may affect the meninges and skull by pressure atrophy it can never invade them or extend to the tissues of the body. On the other hand, the so-called 'dural endothelioma', which is relatively so common as a growth involving arachnoid and dura, frequently shows the power to infiltrate the skull and overlying parts as a malignant neoplasm; but although it may press deeply into the brain it never invades it, being restrained as effectively in the one direction as is the neural glioma in the other. The behaviour of these two tumours has long been familiar, but seems always to have been accepted as very much a matter of course. It is perhaps more reasonable to regard it as one of the most significant anomalies in the whole of pathology.

Our final pathological illustration takes us back to the peripheral nerve. We have already seen that this is the only part of the nervous system where a breach of insulation produces immediate and definite disturbance of function. The neurilemma seems fortunately, however, to be an exceedingly effective barrier between neural and somatic tissues. There is clinical evidence that a relatively slight subcutaneous injury can lead to the formation of a neuro-fibroma presumably through damage to the neurilemma; but this is a rare event of little practical importance, and failing gross injury the insulatory mechanism is wholly satisfactory. That this is the result of effective restraint rather than inertia on the side of the nervous system is perhaps shown by that fortunately rare complaint multiple neuro-fibromatosis or Reckling-hausen's disease. In this condition it has been shown that every fibromatous formation, localized or diffuse, contains nerve fibrils which, presumably by their irritant qualities, have given rise to the fibrosis, much as might a foreign body or a micro-organism of highly attenuated virulence. It seems clear that it is the presence on a large scale of nerve fibrils outside their normal insulating sheath which is the proximate cause of the morbid state. It may be doubted whether the neural leakage is a primary manifestation or is due to an essential weakness or collapse of the insulating function of the neurilemma. Whether the failure of this sheath is primary or secondary, absolute or relative, no one who has seen a severe case of the disease can doubt that any general collapse of the peripheral insulatory mechanism makes the life of its unfortunate subject almost insupportable.

F

Insulation and the Physiology of Pain

I have already called attention to the remarkable fact that there is one kind of sensory fibre which ends in a free arborization in naked contact with the tissues. Our last task in dealing with the insulation of the nervous system is to examine a little more in detail the striking anomaly that in their end-organs the pain fibres make this unique exception to the rule that sensory fibres are insulated up to and including their end-organs.

This anatomical uniqueness of the pain fibre in its end-organ is matched by the uniqueness of the physiological characters of pain sensibility, and it is very natural that we should desire to correlate these two anomalies. Pain sensibility is remarkable in three respects: first, in the quality of the sensation itself; secondly, in its threshold of sensitiveness; and thirdly, in the nature of its appropriate stimuli. (*a*) The *sensation of pain* is peculiar in that it has a sudden and as it were explosive way of bursting into consciousness, in that it calls urgently and often irresistibly for some kind of motor response, and in that it is in its very nature distracting so as to be incompatible with quiet contemplation or steady judgement. (*b*) The *threshold for pain* stimuli is remarkably high, so that in comparison with other forms of common sensibility the stimulus has to be relatively energetic to call forth the characteristic sensation. (*c*) The *stimuli* that call forth pain sensations are remarkable for being very miscellaneous. In every other kind of sensibility but pain, the normal response is to a single well defined physical change—pressure is evoked by weight, touch by movement, cold by loss of heat, warmth by access of heat. The ordinary stimulants of pain, on the other hand, such as pressure, pin-pricks, cold, heat, and the electric current, make up a thoroughly odd class, the members of which show no common character. They are all capable of producing the characteristic sensation before, and usually long before, an intensity of stimulation is reached that can be shown to be harmful. That many of the stimuli would be harmful in greater intensities can scarcely, therefore, be regarded as forming a common physical basis, but must rather be explained as merely a consequence of the normally high threshold.

When we consider these peculiarities we can hardly regard them as those of a highly differentiated mechanism, but rather as those of one relatively crude. All sensibility may well have been of this kind in organisms to which the distracting explosive qualities of the sensation would be no detriment. If we look upon the peculiarities of pain as an evidence of crudity rather than of differentiation it is relatively easy to correlate them with the uninsulated end-organ of the pain fibre, which we must regard as less differentiated and cruder than the complex end-organs of the other fibres. Pain sensibility would thus owe its special character to being the function of a nerve fibre of a peculiar kind, which while relatively insensitive responds in an exaggerated way when its threshold is reached. Presumably these characters are to be associated with the uninsulated end-organ, and we may suspect that it is this lack of insulation which gives to the fibre its characteristic features of blunt sensitivity and emphatic response.

We possess a possible source of further light on this problem in the phenomena that accompany the recovery of function in sensory nerves after division and immediate suture. It is well known that this process, as observed under experimental conditions in the human subject by at least three independent groups of investigators, is accompanied by remarkable modifications in all forms of sensibility. It is impossible to refer to these modifications in detail, but it gives them in a broadly approximate way—and I speak from actual personal experience of them—to say that they are generally in the direction of the peculiarities shown by normal pain; in other words, the modified sensations compared with the normal are more explosive and more urgent, they have a higher threshold, and they call for some kind of motor response. The explanation of these and the other modifications that are to be observed during recovery of sensory nerves has differed with different investigators. It is far too much a matter of detail to discuss these differing hypotheses here, but there is one criticism to be offered of some that is relevant to the general attitude we have tried to support. This criticism is that there has been a tendency to approach the problem in too abstract a way. It has been assumed that the question is one of the mere return of functions that are present in the normal and in the form in which they are then present— modifications in the character of sensation being ascribed to such factors as the order of return and the rate of return of different functions, and the modification in character of one form of sensibility to the presence or absence of another. This is to assume that the processes and incidents of regeneration itself have nothing to say to the problem; and that the struggle between the advancing nerve fibres and the reaction they arouse from the line of suture onwards can be ignored. To take it for granted that the naked growing fibres can pass through this difficult and prolonged ordeal without any alteration in their function, and to limit the problem in this way to strictly and exclusively neural factors, seems to me a method less concrete and practical than the case demands.

An alternative hypothesis, which is at any rate more comprehensive and more simple, can, however, be put forward. The general tendency of all forms of sensation yielded by a regenerating nerve to develop a certain resemblance to pain reminds us that regenerating fibres resemble pain fibres in a lack of complete insulation. It is probable, therefore, that imperfect insulation tends to render all fibres less sensitive than normal, but more apt when effectually stimulated to respond in an exaggerated explosive way. With the advance of regeneration the fibres serving touch, heat, and cold, become once more connected with end-organs, and then their insulation, by the junction of the neurilemma with the capsule of the end-organ, can be completed. The completely insulated fibre, having lost its temporary resemblance to the pain fibre, becomes once more sensitive to the finer stimuli and ceases to yield exaggerated responses.

The process of regeneration thus seems capable of causing a regression of function in all kinds of nerve fibres to a cruder type that in the normal is represented only by pain. This regression occurs because during regeneration insulation must necessarily be defective. According to this hypothesis normal pain and the sensibility of regenerating nerves give us an insight into the ancestry of common sensation. Primitive sensibility of all kinds we may suppose to have been like pain in us; it had a relatively high threshold, but it was effective because its sensations were urgent and explosive and, of course (also like pain in us), were exactly localized. Among such sensations fine discrimination was plainly impossible. With the development of the completely insulated nerve and end-organ the fibres thus equipped became capable of yielding sensation to finer and to specialized stimuli, and of a quality no longer explosive but able to be submitted to discrimination; at the same time the large number of pain nerves remained in their primitive state to warn the body of strong stimuli by urgent sensations among which there was no power and no need for discrimination because their function was to excite immediate response.

The great and manifest difference between the vertebrate and the invertebrate nervous systems is that the former is centralized and the latter is scattered throughout the body. The facts I have quoted and the inferences I have drawn suggest the hypothesis that, side by side with centralization and rendering it possible, insulation also must have proceeded. Insulation on the one hand must have been made increasingly necessary by the growing differentiation of neural from somatic tissues, and on the other hand must have helped to sharpen this very difference. It is not, therefore, surprising that a function so fundamental is not only recognizable in the structure and behaviour of the normal nervous system, but is also evidently at work in morbid processes and constitutes at once a help and a limitation to the work of the surgeon.

THE FUNCTIONS OF THE HUMAN SKULL[1]

THE development of science involves the two processes of collecting facts and of elucidating their relations. In the early days common experience so abounded with unrelated facts that an alert and contemplative mind was an adequate equipment for the man of science and could readily find material for generalization. Knowledge was like an unexploited gold-field, in which the mere attentive wanderer might pick up nuggets of the metal. So were made the earliest discoveries in mathematics, astronomy, and physics. When the surface of the field no longer yielded such finds, the digger with his simple and homely outfit could still from easily accessible deposits gather with his own hand gold dust by the ounce and pound. This was the Golden Age of science; it lasted somewhere about two hundred years, and was nobly marked near its beginning by the *Principia* and near its end by the *Origin of Species*. It was the day of the individual digger, of simple apparatus and the still obvious predominance of the worker's mental quality over every accessory circumstance. It was a time in which relatively simple efforts in the collection of facts might have great results. Looking back at it we discern as a characteristic object Wollaston with his laboratory on a tea-tray, and as a characteristic incident Hans Christian Oersted noticing in 1819 the deflection of the magnetic needle by an electric current—an experiment it would not be very extravagant to call the most important event of the nineteenth century; or as not less characteristic Joseph Fraunhofer in 1814 observing and

---

[1] Lecture delivered before the Anthropological Society of University College, London, on 25 Jan. Reprinted from *Nature*, 6 April 1929.

thinking it worth while to map out the dark lines in the solar spectrum—a dull-looking task that was, however, ultimately to yield a veritable measuring-rod for the universe and a most effective probe of even its stupendous depths.

At the present day what we may call the surface deposits of truth seem almost everywhere to have been worked over, and ours is the time of the thousand-yard shaft, the mile-long gallery, the battery of stamps, and the pennyweight yield to the ton. The mere collection of facts has become a difficult and elaborate enterprise, to which the solitary worker is rarely equal. In almost every branch of science complex equipments are necessary, the mere use of which may need years of training. Even genius itself is no longer inspired by the falling apples and spouting kettles of the Golden Age; the powers of Einstein are called out by the quintessential zero of the Michelson-Morley experiment, or those of Bohr by the incredible vacancies of the atom.

Since the merely observational half of the scientific act has become so formidable, it is natural that the other half that comes of the speculative, contemplative, and relating turn of mind should as such have sunk somewhat in general esteem. It is perhaps correct to say that, among scientific people, work of any general speculative kind is a little under suspicion unless it is closely associated with actual observation as well, and that anyone who tries to correlate large groups of facts is unlikely to be listened to with great attention unless he has been concerned at any rate to some extent in the collection of the facts themselves. This attitude of the mind is on the whole sound and practical, but it should perhaps be qualified by two small reservations. In the first place, the justified predominance of observation may lead to a certain frigidity towards ideas as such, and even some risk of the automatic rejection of them.

In the second place, it must be remembered that there are still some few 'alluvial' deposits left unexhausted in the gold-field of truth. Here the observational side of scientific work may seem when judged by modern standards primitive and 'uneconomic', and yet it may be capable of yielding appreciable finds. One such deposit is the great range of human behaviour, in which we all can be adequately skilled observers and need no more than the critically selective and relating turn of mind. Other such opportunities are apt to occur along the line where two fields of observation meet. Medicine has many such lines of meeting with the sciences, and its contact with anthropology is one of the most obvious. Medical men are interested in the same animal as are anthropologists and have to study it with some intensity.

When we study the boundary zone of two adjoining departments of knowledge, we may expect to find what instruction we are to get not so much in learning strictly ordered and documented facts as in getting fresh points of view; we may hope that the well-established and matter-of-course fact or principle from one side of the line may prove new and illuminating when viewed from the other side.

In such a study, then, we shall do well not to be too exacting in proof or too systematic in method. We must be willing to accept new light where we can find it, and to remember the old paradox that in science the primary duty of ideas is to be useful and interesting even more than to be 'true'. We must be ready to entertain ideas freely and fairly, and no less ready to discard them without regret, glad enough when we gain an unexpected glint from 'the blank face of familiar things'. It will be with very limited pretensions, therefore, that certain considerations derived from surgical experience will be set out here. Nothing could be less dogmatic than the spirit in which they are put forward or more submissive to the principle of the aphorism, 'Do not believe new ideas; use them'.

While the essential object of all biological knowledge is the elucidation of function, the work of the surgeon is actually engaged in the direct study of function in a very special degree. He is concerned with the human body solely as a going concern and his unique object is to keep it going. In regard to the cranium, he has no direct interest in its size, its form, its types, its indices; he limits himself, with what for the anthropologist must seem a certain crudity, to the question what does it do? In the briefest possible terms, the cranium is to the surgeon the *capsule* and *the skeleton of the brain*.

The Capsule of the Brain

It is not usual to regard the brain as among the encapsuled organs, but to do so brings out an interesting aspect of its functional relations with the skull. If we consider encapsuled organs in general we at once see that the rigidity of the capsule is an important character. In regard to it, organs may be divided into three groups. In the first, which may be called the normal type and is represented by the kidney and spleen, the capsule is fully extensible; in the second, represented by the testis, only very slightly extensible; and in the third, represented by the brain and skull, it is absolutely rigid to all physiological forces. Such conditions have necessary and very important effects on the mechanics of the circulation in the various organs. There is of course a primary need for the flow of blood through any tissue to be continuous; this is effected in organs of the first group by the extensibility of the capsule permitting pulsation and elastic recoil to occur. In the case of the brain, however, a different mechanism is necessary. The brain itself expands with each arterial pulse, but, as the skull is unyielding, room must be made at each pulsation by the expulsion of a corresponding volume of the low pressure intracranial fluids. This is why the veins leaving the skull and the cerebrospinal fluid in the subarachnoid space of the spinal cord show arterial pulsation.

The mechanism is adequate, but the margin by which it is so is not very large. After violent exertion, when the range of pulsation of the brain is at its widest, we are apt to be conscious of an unpleasant thudding in the head, which shows that the brain can only just find room for its circulatory excursions. Again, if one has a slight headache it is at once aggravated by exertion.

This circulatory peculiarity is fundamental in cerebral pathology and makes it possible to say that, apart from purely destructive processes, all cerebral symptoms are of circulatory origin.

We may briefly inquire into how this comes about. The low pressure outflow that must accompany each arterial pulsation is chiefly in the form of venous blood. For it to occur the flow of blood in the veins must be quite free. But the pressure in the veins is very low, so that the least abnormal swelling of the brain or part of it causes collapse and obstruction of a greater or less venous territory. Thereupon further swelling from venous congestion occurs and the disturbance of function becomes progressive.

The brain is thus uniquely sensitive to any pathological change in its bulk. When an organ like the kidney is bruised and swells, it matters very little how soon or if ever it gets back to its normal size. When the brain has been bruised, it must get back to its normal size or its circulation will remain permanently disturbed. A simple bruise of no ultimate importance to an organ with a yielding capsule, is thus a relatively serious matter with the brain. The great difficulty with which the brain recovers from even simple injuries that cause swelling is one of the most important functional consequences of its rigid encapsulation by the skull.[1]

THE DEFENSIVE FUNCTION OF THE SKULL

It is still a widespread opinion, even to some extent among medical men, that fracture of the skull is the most important feature of head injury, and that if the skull is not fractured not much harm can have been done. There is no more complete delusion. Fracture of the skull is usually an insignificant element in a head injury, and nothing has done more to limit the knowledge of trustworthy principle than the traditional reverence for it.

A fracture means that the skull has been distorted until the limit of its elasticity has been passed. It is the distortion, and not the crack that may or may not ensue, that is important.

Now surgical experience in Great Britain shows that the skull is susceptible to considerable degrees of distortion by even only moderately severe external violence. Because immediate and dramatic effects are not always produced, and because of the superstition about the significance of fracture, it is apt to be assumed that the average European cranium is on the whole very successful in preserving the brain within it from the effects of quite severe violence. Since the nature of

[1] It is interesting to notice that the testis—the only other organ in the body that approaches the brain in the rigidity of its capsule—shows the same susceptibility to minor injuries. As is well known, it may undergo complete atrophy after a simple bruise.

what are called the minor injuries of the brain has been better understood, this faith in the beneficent fortitude of the skull has been considerably shaken. We now know that the skull in its protective function is only moderately effective. It is liable to bend under local violence and to permit of a localized bruising of the brain beneath; it is also liable in appropriate circumstances, especially such as falls on the head, to a far more serious general distortion. This general distortion causes the very interesting instantaneous and transient paralysis known as concussion of the brain, and is also apt to produce a widespread bruising of the brain substance that is of great practical importance. It is important to note that all the evidence points to actual distortion of the skull being the immediate cause of most if not all injuries of the brain. There is no reason to suppose that injury is commonly if ever produced by the brain being thrown about inside an undistorted skull. It is probably true to say in so many words, no distortion of skull, no injury of the brain.[1]

This liability to relatively easy distortion seems to be in some special degree a character of the modern European skull. It appears to be fairly clear that in some races the resistiveness is decidedly higher. For example, the negro, judged by purely clinical, that is functional considerations, is little liable to receive cerebral contusions from the moderate degrees of violence that an Englishman could not endure with impunity. The willingness of the negro to use his head as a battering-ram has often been described, and it is said that an experienced policeman will use his truncheon on the head of a negro less hopefully than he would use it on an English head.

[1] A contrary opinion is perhaps encouraged by the use of the time-honoured and now ineradicable phrases 'concussion of the brain' in English and 'Hirnerschütterung' in German.

We arrive then at the position that the modern European skull is demonstrably far from completely effective in its protective function, and that this defect is not shared by all other races.

It will be noticed that we are not at all concerned so far with the anatomy of skulls. It may or may not be possible to show a difference in the thickness or rigidity of European and negro skulls. The test of function is far more delicate and trustworthy than that of structure, and it seems to show that a clear difference exists.

We have already seen that the bony capsule of the brain is a serious hindrance to recovery from minor injuries, so that the skull and brain mechanism is satisfactory only when the former is highly effective as a protective covering. Once the protective function is impaired the physiological disadvantages of the arrangement becomes fully manifest. It seems clear, then, that the present functional relation of brain and skull—plainly disadvantageous as it is—must be the result of some strong evolutionary tendency or must be accounted for by some advantage that compensates for it.

In a very broad and general way, it does appear to be the fact that there has been an evolutionary tendency towards a reduction in the massiveness of the human cranium; there can be no doubt that the modern European cranium is in comparison with many of its predecessors remarkably light and thin. It is not improbable, therefore, that a tendency towards the lightening of the cranium is an inherent character of the race and progressive. It is natural, therefore, to ask how far such a process could conceivably go. The European skull has already discarded a good deal of its protective rigidity; is a rigid cranium a necessary structure?

THE SKELETAL FUNCTION OF THE SKULL

Without considering any other matter but function, this question can be given a perfectly definite answer. However much more of its protective massiveness the skull may lose, it must always maintain enough rigidity to preserve its form. This is because it is a function of the skull, not the less important for being usually over-looked, to support the brain. If we make in the treatment of injury or disease a considerable hole in the skull, and after healing of the scalp is complete the intra-cranial tension is normal, we find a tendency for the soft parts to sink into the cranial opening. This depression is most marked when the subject is standing and usually quite filled up when he is lying down. With an opening 3 or 4 in. across, the depression may perhaps reach a depth of as much as $1\frac{1}{2}$ in. at its centre. The larger the opening the greater the depression; and it is clear, therefore, that the exposed brain, when the intra-cranial tension is at its lowest, cannot support the atmospheric pressure and actually collapses under it. In certain cases the subjects of openings in the skull suffer severely from the exaggerated movements of the brain that in them accompany changes of posture. Such symptoms are always abolished when the opening is closed by restoration of the skull.

In the cranium, in fact, the vertebrate has rediscovered the principle of the external skeleton and exploited it in a remarkably interesting way that may be worth a moment's consideration. What may be called the constructional problems of such an immense mass of neural tissues as the brain are very complex. The obvious way of supporting a large mass of soft consistence would be the provision of a stiff stroma of ordinary connective tissue. Such a solution is inadmissible for very definite reasons. In the first place, direct contact between meso-blastic and neural tissues is a physiological impossibility, so that every strand of the hypothetical connective tissue stroma would have to be clothed, as is every cerebral vessel, with a so-called 'perivascular lymphatic' to its finest ramifications. At a moderate estimate this might double the bulk of the whole organ. Again, the presence of an elaborate and alien fibrous network would im-mensely complicate the system of intercommunication, which is the very essence of the brain as it is. How neat a solution of the problem does the exo-skeleton provide. With it, it is possible for the brain to be made up almost entirely of actual functional elements, and for the utmost complexity of communication to exist while the bulk of the whole organ is kept within bounds.

The Meaning of the Vulnerable Skull

We have seen that the low strength of the modern European skull is shown by actual experience to be pro-ducing serious effects in the way of a high susceptibility to disabling injuries of the brain. To discuss the mean-ing of this remarkable and perhaps a little disturbing state of affairs it is necessary to enter into some rather general considerations.

There can be no doubt that in the growth side by side of the cranium and the brain, the latter is the predominant partner, and what it needs the former must on the whole provide. If the skull had no other function whatever but to be the capsule and skeleton of the brain, the correspon-dence would be absolute and every least developmental variation of the brain would be accurately accommodated by the skull. Now the skull or even the cranium does have other functions to fulfil than those concerned with the brain. It is involved with the muscles of the trunk, with the apparatus of mastication, with the respiratory tract. The provision for these accessory needs must, it seems reasonable to suppose, have some influence however minor on the growth of the cranium, and act as some restraint however minute on the control of it by the brain, and therefore on the freedom of variation of the latter. When, therefore, the skull is very massive and deeply involved with accessory functions, when it gives attachment to large neck muscles, when it is ridged and fortified for a heavy masticatory apparatus, the freedom of the brain to develop minor variations is perhaps less complete than when the cranium is stripped to the condition of a mere cerebral capsule.

Since it is possible that free variability of the brain through a very small range is of value in fitting man for a complex civilization, it seems not a very extravagant supposition that the freeing of the skull from accessory functions has been a factor in human evolution.

EVOLUTION OF THE BRAIN AND SKULL

In considering the evolutionary process in general, then, we have to think not merely of a progressive expansion of the cranium to accommodate the increasing brain, but also of a growing independence of the cranium.

It seems obvious that the anterior end of the segmental animal was the inevitable site for the chief nucleus of a centralized nervous system. The same region was equally inevitably annexed for the entry to the respiratory and the digestive tracts. An interesting series of complications has ensued from this necessary crowding of function into one extremity. It does not seem too fantastic to see two tendencies constantly at work and in conflict—the tendency on one hand to make use of the brain skeleton for functions connected with other systems, and on the other the struggle of the brain for autonomy and freedom from these burdens. Wherever the former tendency has been definitely the stronger, the progress of the brain has been arrested and the animal has found itself in an evolutionary blind alley. The most striking illustration of this process has been in connexion with apparatus of defence and attack. Such apparatus has a natural and inevitable localization near the digestive inlet and at the anterior end of the animal. Nature in her experiments with horns, antlers, fangs, and tusks has found the skull waiting as a convenient foundation for these useful but enslaving structures. The ancestors of man, with the steady avoidance of specialization to which he so largely owes his zoological position, kept their craniums free from such encumbrances.

It was, however, probably the beginning of the upright posture that was the decisive change in favour of the independent skull. It has not, so far as I know, been much remarked upon that the upright posture changes the whole mechanics of attack and defence from that of the quadruped. The head is withdrawn from the front of the animal, and thus being no longer available as a foundation for offensive or defensive structures, the cranium is at last and finally safe from them. Another and more familiar way in which the cranium was helped by the upright posture to free itself from accessory functions was in the limitation in the movements of the mandible that necessarily ensued. With a poised instead of a slung skull, the mouth can no longer be opened freely enough for the aggressive use of fangs. Thereupon the cranium is no longer called upon to find attachment for the correspondingly massive muscles.

When we see an evolutionary tendency so strong as that seems to be which has stripped and lightened the

THE FUNCTIONS OF THE HUMAN SKULL 83

cranium until it has reached the degree of fragility and simplification seen in the modern European, we are inclined to ask whether even yet its force is exhausted. There are perhaps signs that even now the cranium is, so to say, intolerant even of the light burden of accessory function it still has to bear. It is scarcely possible to be familiar with the lower jaw of the modern English without wondering whether the unexhausted tendency we have been considering is not at work to free the cranium even of the temporal muscle. It is clear that the molar region of the mandible is shrinking, and experience already suggests that eight fully erupted molar teeth are nearer the actual normal than twelve. Since the temporal muscle is especially concerned with the use of the molars, it is perhaps permissible to wonder whether it, rather than the jaw, is not the real object of evolutionary attack.

The tenuity of much of the foregoing speculation must be obvious. The argument, however, makes no attempt to be rigorous, and is intended to be illustrative rather than demonstrative. The object of it has been to find out whether the old-fashioned method of general qualitative survey might not in so favourable a situation as the frontier between two branches of knowledge, present the familiar facts of one side of the line in a way that would have freshness and perhaps interest on the other.

ART AND SCIENCE IN MEDICINE[1]

EVEN the most assiduous workman will from time to time stand back to get a more general view of his work and to contemplate its wider relations. Indeed, such intermissions are necessary if he is to escape the tyranny of detail, and they need only the defence of a reasonable infrequency and of being actually employed in their ostensible purpose. However austerely, therefore, we may hold the view that a school is best occupied in doing its job of teaching, we shall probably be willing to allow it the privilege and even to enjoin on it the duty of an occasional suspension of this task.

This is such an occasion. For the moment, the teacher has ceased to teach and—even more anomalous—the student has ceased to learn. We stand back from the enormous detail of medicine, we take breath, we allow our eyes to accommodate for distant vision again, and we try to recover the sense of belonging to the world at large. If the occasion needs excuse, we may remind ourselves that in this school at any rate such indulgences are beneficently rare. We shall do better, however, if we give it a more positive justification. The greatest we could provide would be to make these moments taken from educational routine give us a more active consciousness that this institution lives and can survive only by virtue of its corporate unity. It is not necessary for me to inform an audience so largely and recently adept in physiology that corporate unity depends on freedom of communication among the parts, or to argue the point that the physiological fact has its convincing analogy in

---

[1] Being the Address delivered at the opening of the Session, 1932–3, at the U.C.H. Medical School, on Tuesday, 4 Oct. 1932. Reprinted from *University College Hospital Magazine*, Sept.–Oct. 1932.

social institutions. Now it is an anomaly in the practice of education that communication between teacher and pupil, on the freedom of which it would seem success must depend, is not always regarded as worthy of every encouragement. The physiologist will not be surprised to find that education is unsatisfactory in proportion as general understanding between teacher and pupil is uneasy and restricted. Fortunately medical education is perhaps least of all subject to this limitation. What it does suffer in this respect is the result of inadvertence or inattention rather than of deliberate policy. We can be fairly assured that communication between teacher and student is not to-day seriously restricted in the supposed interests of dignity and discipline on the one hand, or of independence and self-assertion on the other. Indeed, a medical school is one of the few places of education where communication is constantly supported by the certainty the student may feel that the teacher is always willing to teach and by the similar certainty the teacher may feel that the student, in spite of whatever appearance to the contrary, is always willing to learn.

Nevertheless, it is the principal function of an occasion such as this, to assert and exemplify the corporate unity of the school, and to assert and exemplify the fundamental truth that all its members of whatever seniority, and whether ostensibly teachers or taught, are equally indispensable to its healthy life.

A minor function of this assembly is that which I am instructed to fulfil. That function is to lay before you any considerations I can produce that may be of help to those engaged in, or about to begin, the hospital part of their training. A strictly practical task, and one that, though it may lead us into certain theoretical considerations,

I shall approach with a strictly practical object. I shall
confine myself to a single and small part of the subject,
and attempt to get some understanding of the relation between the earlier part of medical education
and that carried on in the hospital. If that sounds a dry
programme I can at any rate point for reassurance to
what it omits of the topics normal to these exercises.
There will be no reminiscences; there will be no com-
parisons of the students of to-day with the students of
another generation; above all, we shall not discuss the
curriculum. It seems almost an impiety for the giver of
an introductory address to decline to discuss the curriculum, but I shall ask you for this hour to regard that formidable structure as a natural object. Whatever views
we may have about the necessity for change in it, the
curriculum gives the conditions under which, as teacher
and taught, we have for the moment to work. We do
not therefore need for our present purpose the usual
attitude of critical inquisition, but rather the mood
taught us by experience of our climate and of human
nature—the mood of philosophic resignation.

From College to Hospital

What is the most important event in a medical student's life might be variously defined. If we limit ourselves to his mental development there is good ground
for supposing that his most important experience will
be the transition from what are called his preliminary
studies to hospital work. He will find that this passage
which he has been perhaps taught to look forward to as
a natural and easy phase of growth, has brought him
into a world of strange methods and odd points of view.
The fresh environment is likely to affect him as not only
bewildering in its crowd of new detail, but as confused

in its very nature. These experiences, however, may be or should be made to be, the most interesting intellectual adventure of his life.

I would ask you to pause a moment on that phrase 'intellectual adventure'. It is a coin in the ordinary exchange of speech familiar enough to have got a little worn and flat, and no longer to give a sharp strong image of the idea it should contain. The temper that seeks adventure in the physical world is one we are all ready to admire, though we are perhaps in our hearts a little relieved that the modern world is supposed to offer few opportunities for its exercise. It differs from the temper of most of us in possessing a discontent with the familiar strong enough to break through custom and sacrifice the security of ordinary life. To get away from the tedium of the usual it will risk strangeness, difficulty and danger, pursue impossible objects and seek vanishing goals. Whether or not it is true that the age of the adventurer in the physical world is now closed, adventure in the world of thought is still open to every soul that is not wholly tamed and in love with the cage. It has always been more difficult than adventure in the ordinary sense, and it is becoming more difficult every day. Uniformity of thought is increasingly the apparent goal and demand of civilization; education has no use for the fires of rebellion, and even science itself is not above lending an occasional hand at the fire-engine. Still there burns on in most of us a small wild spark. I advise you to nourish it as a precious possession. Do not, however, be under any misapprehension. Really to think for oneself is as strange, difficult, and dangerous as any adventure, and, as the wise ones say, 'it will do you no good'; but, like virtue—which it does not otherwise greatly resemble—it will be its own reward.

From Physiology to Medicine

When the student enters the hospital he comes from the acquisition of a remarkable equipment. He has been introduced to the general principles and meaning of science; and he has had a prolonged and detailed training in the structure and functions of the animal, and especially of the human body. These exercises have had a double purpose; they have given him a knowledge of the normal out of which it is to be supposed his studies of disease will naturally develop, and they have trained his mind so that he may be supposed to approach the problems of the abnormal with the confidence of the mental athlete. This latter function of his studies is the famous mental discipline, a convenience it may perhaps be well to examine a little more closely.

The training received in the earlier studies and especially perhaps in the physiological laboratory is, of course, that of becoming familiar with the method of experimental science—the method which beyond all shadow of doubt is the most effective implement for the advancement of knowledge ever invented by man. Now the essential requirement of this great method is that the conditions of an experiment should be as nearly capable of complete specification as is possible. Necessarily, therefore, the effort of the experimenter is that every observation is as much simplified as the conditions allow. An ideal experiment is thus a piece of experience so simplified that all the circumstances are capable of full specification. However much ingenuity, judgement, and knowledge may go to the design of an experiment, the actual observation itself gains in validity by the extent to which human skill, judgement, and faculty can be eliminated from it. This then is the characteristic contribution of experimental science to mental discipline

—the lesson that experience is useful for the discovery of truth in so far as its conditions can be specified, measured, and controlled. The lesson well assimilated will give to its recipient an invaluable touchstone by which supposedly established facts and theories can be tested. Its general effect on his mind in the present state of medicine is likely perhaps to make him a little doubtful of the validity of a large part of medical doctrine and a little pessimistic about its value.

Carrying then in one hand a wide and exact knowledge of the normal and in the other the principles of experimental science the student enters upon his hospital work. In the matter of knowledge and in the matter of method he is about to meet with surprises which will be great perhaps in direct proportion to the thoroughness of his previous studies. Let us consider first how far his work upon the normal helps him in dealing with the sick. He will find that but few of his patients are suffering from diseases of which he has already some fundamental knowledge and that he sees relatively few cases of acromegaly, myxoedema, rickets, osteomalacia, xerophthalmia, scurvy, or even beri-beri. He will find that the great majority of his patients complain of one or more of six things—a feeling of illness, pain, loss of appetite, nausea or vomiting, sleeplessness, constipation. If he looks to his knowledge of the normal for light upon these symptoms, he will notice that he has been taught little about the processes of which they are the perversion, and that most of them have scarcely been mentioned. When you ask your gardener why a certain bed has not been weeded or a certain edging not cut, he will tell you that he has not come round to it. When we ask the physiologist what is the sense of well being, what is sleep, what is appetite, even what is a normal action of the bowels, he gives us the perfectly just and proper answer that he has not come round to these subjects. The fact is physiology is an independent science which must follow its own inspiration, finding it sometimes here, sometimes there, and only occasionally in medicine.

In 1754 Dr. James Lind, in his *Treatise on the Scurvy*, showed what scurvy is due to, and advised its treatment, as we do to-day, by lemon juice. To give some sort of a time scale for the effects of this disclosure I may mention a small scrap of naval history. The Lords of the Admiralty, concerned at the existence of an agency for the destruction of seamen more effective than the enemy's guns, and with the deference for hygiene characteristic of all military bodies, adopted Lind's recommendations for the Navy after an interval of only forty years. But it was 150 years before physiology, having taken that time to come round to it, discovered the existence of vitamin C. Thus it took not forty years but a century and a half for one of the clearest and most direct hints from medicine to produce an effect in the physiological world.

Such phenomena in the natural history of knowledge are of course in no way a reproach to physiology. It was in the structure of events that an experience of medicine, which now seems so rich with intimations, should fail for so long to reach and inspire the physiologist; it was also no less in the structure of events that those engaged in medicine and fully open to these hints should have neither the training nor the inclination that could have led them to submit the familiar facts to experimental analysis. Of these two natural checks to the progress of medical science—the relative insensitiveness of physiology to direct inspiration by medicine on the one hand,

and on the other the inaptitude of those engaged in medicine to make full use of exact experiment—the former is likely to be lasting while the latter is likely to be removed. For physiology will continue its independent course. Sometimes, in such tasks as the energy exchanges of nerve it will work on the very limit of medical vision, at others it will approach with some noble gift in its hand like insulin or the doctrine of the deficiency diseases. Medicine more and more understanding the lost opportunities of past years will take to itself the methods of experimental science and lead the *direct* attack on its own problems. Meanwhile the practical upshot of these considerations for the student is that in a large part of medicine he can at present hope for little direct light from his earlier studies. It is, moreover, on the most ordinary and the most frequent phenomena of medicine that the illumination of physiology is most dimly cast—on pain, the commonest of all symptoms without exception, and on functions so enormously important to the patient as those of appetite and sleep.

From Science to Art

The most interesting experience, however, of the student on entering the hospital is undoubtedly the change of method. The austere simplicity of laboratory reasoning has gone. He will be expected to accept judgements based on mere unspecified experience, on intuition, on delicately balanced probabilities all imperfectly defined. He will be shocked by what seems an uncritical laxity in the very air, and blush as the improprieties of method he is expected to condone. He will have passed in fact from the world of science to that of a practical art.

That medicine is essentially an art is being a good deal insisted on at the present time, and before we agree wholly to that view it would be well to define it a little more precisely. The word 'art' has so many meanings which are so easily and so commonly interchanged that it has to be handled with some care. We can speak of the art of the blacksmith, of the pianist, of the farmer, of the poet, of the sculptor or painter—in each case meaning something different, but in each case with a fringe of significance tending to overlap from use to use. It would be tedious and unnecessary for our purpose here to dissect out the different threads from this plexus of meaning. We can, however, at once discard two meanings the irrelevance of which is plain. On the one hand medicine is not a mere skill, though it includes many skills, such for example, as the art of bandaging and the art of auscultation. On the other hand medicine is clearly not a fine art like that of the painter or the sculptor. From this it can be separated at once by the considerations that its object is not the production of beauty and is determined for the artist and not by him, and that its material is not inert and disposable, but an active factor in the art process. It is sometimes asserted that a surgical operation is or should be a work of art of this kind, fit to rank with those of the painter or sculptor. As I have shown, that proposition does not admit of discussion. It is a product of the intellectual innocence which I think we surgeons may fairly claim to possess, and which is happily not inconsistent with a quite adequate worldly wisdom.

We are left then to conclude that medicine must be classed with what we may call the practical arts, like those of the farmer, the builder, the blacksmith, the joiner, or the sailor. Do not hastily conclude that this definition is derogatory to medicine, for that would be a very crude blunder.

PRACTICAL ARTS AND APPLIED SCIENCES

The genius of man has devised two methods by which his culture is built up and put into use—the practical arts and the applied sciences. There is a fundamental difference both in history and in principle of action between these two. An applied science carries on its tasks by the application of ascertained principles to particular cases. Thus the mechanical engineer designs an engine for a special purpose, and proceeds to construct it in the confident expectation that it will do the work it is designed to do. Indefinable elements in the task there will be few or none, success will therefore depend chiefly on pure systematic knowledge and very little upon judgement, intuition, or personal skill. A practical art has no complete and sure foundation of ascertained principles. Its possessions are made up of separate and fragmentary conquests from the unknown. The items of its knowledge are therefore incompletely definable and are preserved as the traditionary rules of the art. These are not *applied* like scientific principles to the particular case, but are *interpreted* for its treatment in accordance with the judgement, intuition, and personal skill of the artist. It thus comes about that in a practical art satisfactory action is judged not wholly by its object being attained, but by whether the artist followed the established rules, whether, as we say, he proceeded 'secundum artem'. In a true applied science failure can be due only to ignorance, in a practical art where so much is indefinable success as a sole test for correct action is obviously impracticable. To adopt for a practical art the standard of attainment applicable to an applied science is not to improve its status, it is only to convert it into quackery.

In these days of the rapid progress of science and of its application to life it is tempting and fatally easy to become contemptuous of the practical arts. Such an error will be avoided if we try to get a view of these activities in their historical perspective. It seems probable that in the practical arts man made his first serious attempt at the continuous storage of knowledge and the establishment of a progressive culture. Half-seen truths and obscure intuitions cannot be preserved and transmitted as such, but they can be given a relative permanence when embodied in rules of action and sanctioned by tradition. It was in such rules, no doubt, that the earliest practical discoveries of man were kept alive. We are apt to complain of the invincible conservatism of such traditionary arts as medicine and agriculture. As long as a body of knowledge exists as an art, conservatism, whatever its defects, is a quality of functional value and indispensable in the circumstances.

The oldest products of human culture we possess are the flint implements that have come down to us from palaeolithic times. They show how ancient is man's first great discovery in method—the practical art. One of the most astonishing things about these 'immemorial artefacts' is the immense length of time through which the different types persisted. The conservatism of the art that governed their manufacture and gave such secular endurance to individual types was strong indeed, but perhaps only just strong enough to keep alive the uncertain flame of culture itself.

Conservatism then is functional in a practical art, but let this fact remind us that in science it is necessarily meaningless and always and wholly harmful.

We should not conclude these meagre hints of the status of the practical arts without recalling that they have been not only the earliest conservers of knowledge but also the mothers and nurses of science itself. Even the lofty sciences of mathematics and astronomy, for example, were born of the humble art of the surveyor.

The general process of culture seems to be towards the ultimate conversion of practical arts into applied sciences. The more easily definable the conditions the more rapid the transformation. The art of the mechanical engineer is already almost completely transformed, while the work of the electrical engineer had no youth as an art at all but sprang into being as an applied science. Where, however, the conditions are less easily definable then the process is necessarily slow and partial.

The bulk of a doctor's activities remain then in the region of art, and the frontier between it and such ground as science has gained has a certain indistinctness which it should be one of the student's most interesting exercises to define and keep clear. Fashion and the popular voice tend always to exaggerate the conquests of science, and to press the frontier far beyond the line of its actual advance. In refusing to yield to this fallacious pressure the student will do well to remember an assertion which I have already made and which I may be allowed to repeat. It is that a practical art which pretends to be applied science does not thereby show itself to be progressive, it only shows itself to be quackery.

When we compare science and art in medicine we find that, to use a mechanical analogy, the former is enormously the more efficient engine where it is available. Its only necessary fuel is knowledge—given knowledge and the appropriate case, success with a very small margin of error is certain. Medical art on the other

hand is as an engine extravagantly inefficient and needs
every faculty of the doctor to get it to work at all. This
is why it is that he has not only to be taught but to be
trained. By teaching I mean the imparting of knowledge,
and for that we are dependent on our teachers; by training I mean the cultivation of aptitude, and for that we
are dependent on our opportunities and ourselves. It is
here that we see most clearly the difference in the requirements of experimental science and of an art. The
exactitudes of science call for the elimination of human
faculty as far as possible; the lack of exactitude in the
practical art calls for the use and expansion of human
faculty as far as possible. It would be a poor physiologist
who used his eye to estimate the weight of guinea-
pigs or his tongue to measure electric currents; but the
physician who makes the fundamental observation of
medicine and says, 'My clinical instinct tells me that
man is ill', though he uses an instrument with an error
deplorably great, uses the only instrument capable of
making any record at all, and will do well to keep it in
repair.

APTITUDES OF THE DOCTOR

The thread of my argument has led us through considerations which cannot have seemed to promise much
for the uses of daily life. At length, however, it brings
us to a conclusion of a different kind. We see that as
long as medicine is an art, its chief and characteristic
instrument must be human faculty. We come therefore
to the very practical question of what aspects of human
faculty it is necessary for the good doctor to cultivate.
In trying to answer that question we need say nothing
of the many kinds of skill the student will have to acquire; every branch of medicine has its local technique,

H

to master which is a mere matter of practice. I shall call your attention to none of these but only to a few of the more general requirements of practical medicine.

The first to be named must always be the power of attention, of giving one's whole mind to the patient without the interposition of anything of oneself. It sounds simple but only the very greatest doctors ever fully attain it. It is an active process and not either mere resigned listening or even politely waiting until you can interrupt. Disease often tells its secrets in a casual parenthesis.

The second thing to be striven for is intuition. This sounds an impossibility, for who can control that small quiet monitor. But intuition is only inference from experience stored and not actively recalled. For that reason we should acquire experience and more experience. Do not let us submit, however, to the delusion that experience is made up of the events at which we are present. A broadcasting microphone is present at very numerous events but it has no experience. An event experienced is an event perceived, digested, and assimilated into the substance of our being, and the ratio between the number of cases seen and the number of cases assimilated is the measure of experience.

A humbler requirement but one not less necessary is the art of handling living flesh. Here at any rate is something everyone can teach himself. Hands co-ordinated to smooth, firm, and gentle movement are to the sick body the complement of the attentive receptive mind. It yields its secrets to them but denies its secrets to the mutton fist as it does to the beefy mind. We must not use the excuses that patients expect to be hurt, that they accept with resignation the clumsy dressing of wounds, and allow themselves to be examined by a series of crude prods and bangs. When you ask a patient if you are hurting him, nine times out of ten he will reply with touching cheerfulness, 'Not yet, Doctor'. What a succession of iron thumbs is disclosed by that answer! Some extremists have thought that the man who has the handling of sick human bodies should make himself ambidextrous. I do not subscribe to that, but I sometimes think the student would do well to limit himself to the possession of only one left hand.

The last aptitude I shall mention that must be attained by the good doctor is that of handling the sick man's mind. The subject is one that lends itself to clever treatment. I shall ask you, however, to excuse me from trying to be clever and shall make a few plain and practical remarks.

The ordinary patient goes to his doctor because he is in pain or some other discomfort and wants to be comfortable again; he is not in pursuit of the ideal of health in any direct sense. The doctor on the other hand wants to discover the pathological condition and control it if he can. The two are thus to some degree at cross purposes from the first, and unless the affair is brought to an early and happy conclusion this divergence of aims is likely to become more and more serious as the case goes on. The good doctor therefore has to learn to serve two objects at the same time—the diagnosis and treatment of the patient's ailment on one hand, and to keep him comfortable on the other. I speak of keeping the patient comfortable in the broadest possible sense to include matters of the mind as well as of the body; it is an art which the student must teach himself, and the practice of it is one of the worst burdens put upon the doctor by the fact that man is not a reasonable creature. In the exercise of this art he will have to convince the patient

of his interest in the case, he will have to let him feel
that something significant is being done all the time and
he will have to teach him that his object must be health
not comfort. When these purposes are clearly visualized
they are easy enough to attain. The most important is
that the doctor should convince the patient of his personal interest. The simplest way to do this is to be
interested, and the effort will have its reward. To the
deep unreason with which all patients approach the
medicine man, his interest is more potent than knowledge and skill, the latest development in science, or the
utmost virtuosity in art.

I have tried to point to some considerations bearing
on the transition from experimental science to clinical
work in the hope that they may do something to soften
the jar with which these different systems of knowledge
sometimes meet one another. In doing so I have perhaps tended to sharpen the differences between the two
in order to mark the unique value of clinical medicine in
the training of human faculty. Let me add a final word
in the opposite sense.

The invasion of medicine by science has in the past
proceeded from without and from the directions of
physiology and of pathology. Of recent years experimental science has formally established itself within the
field of medicine, deriving its inspiration from the hospital and its strength from the laboratory, and our school
is singularly fortunate in being the actual scene of such
an enterprise. Science is, moreover, influencing medicine
in a third more general and more indirect way: it is
having an effect on methods and making us less willing
to leave the small individual problems of practical
medicine to be decided by vague clinical impressions, by
insignificant statistics, by authority, or by tradition. It

would be of the greatest service to medicine if the determination became general to submit every minor problem of clinical work in which the conditions allow to methods by which an exact decision would be possible. This is a direction in which the thoughts of those who have just come from science to clinical work might very well be turned. Such an activity would give further zest to what I have promised them may be made the most interesting intellectual adventure of their lives.

OBSERVATION AND EXPERIMENT AND THEIR USE IN THE MEDICAL SCIENCES[1]

The Methods of Science in General

THE accumulation of verifiable knowledge, which is the object of science, depends fundamentally on the discovery of invariable sequences of events in the complex and apparently random phenomena of our experience. The obvious method of doing this is that of observation. We study the natural succession of events as they pass before us and observe those resemblances and recurrences which betray an underlying relation. The power of the method has been increased by refinement and elaboration until it can scarcely be recognized in this simple statement of it. Instruments such as the telescope, the microscope, the spectroscope, have increased its range and its precision; completeness and exactitude of record have increased its trustworthiness; and mathematics has given it the power of detecting relations among recorded facts too complex or too obscure to be within range of direct contemplation. But refinement of method, however far it may be carried, can never surmount the limitation by which observation in its very nature is restricted. This limitation is the circumstance that the observer must wait upon the natural occurrence of the phenomena he wishes to study. The phenomena may be too infrequent for their significant recurrence to come within the span of human life, they may be too complex and too closely mixed with irrelevant events for the invariable sequences they possess to be detected.

[1] Reprinted from the *British Medical Journal*, 26 July 1930.

Science has found a means of escape from the limitations of the method of observation in the method of experiment. Partial as the solution of the problem must be admitted to be it has proved of the highest value—of such value, indeed, that its own limitations tend sometimes to be a little overlooked. It will therefore perhaps be useful to examine more closely the relations of the two methods.

The method of experiment seeks to free the man of science from the arbitrary natural distribution of the phenomena he wishes to study. It seeks to give him the required phenomena at command and unmixed with irrelevant events which may modify the essential facts and confuse the study of them. Experiment, then, isolates the event to be studied from the common order of nature, and causes it to occur in circumstances as far as possible simplified and subject to specification.

Applicability of Experiment

Certain sciences have not merely benefited by experiment, but have been created by it. This is true of physics and of chemistry, and is so nearly true of physiology as scarcely to need discussion. In all these sciences experience has proved that the laboratory 'event' is as good as the natural 'event', and that the simplification needed for experimental precision is not necessarily accompanied by distortion of the phenomena concerned. On the whole perhaps it is surprising that physiology has been able successfully to isolate for study so many of the phenomena of living organisms, but of the fact there can be no doubt.

Regarded as subjects for experiment certain sciences stand at the opposite extreme to the position occupied by chemistry and physics. Such are astronomy, geology, meteorology. In the material of their sciences the scale of time and space and the forces concerned are so large that it is usually impossible to produce in the laboratory conditions approaching those of the natural event. These sciences therefore must be, and apparently must continue to be, primarily observational. This is, however, by no means to deny that they can and do have useful relations with experimental methods, though these relations may be less direct than in other sciences. In geology we may, for example, study in the laboratory some of the elements in the process of metamorphism, though we can command no more than an almost negligible fraction of the time and the force that have gone to the formation of metamorphic rocks in nature. In meteorology, again, we may study the differences of electric potential that are produced by the breaking up of falling water-drops, but we must remain almost infinitely far from the scale and magnitude of a natural thunderstorm. In astronomy, a science of whose debt to experimental work there can also be no question, the impossibility of reproducing in the laboratory the conditions of the natural event is still more apparent.

Thus in geology, meteorology, and astronomy experiment occupies the position of the small-scale model and is therefore subject in its degree to the defects of the argument from analogy. These sciences must in fact be described as sciences of observation and *collateral* experiment, and have very plain methodical differences from the sciences of *direct* experiment such as physics and chemistry.

Experiment in the Biological Sciences

Physiology has been included here among the sciences of direct experiment, and there can be no doubt of the thoroughness and success with which it has established itself there. It has been hinted, however, that the case of physiology is to some extent different from that of the other sciences of direct experiment, and its brilliant evolution has had to overcome difficulties special to it. The living organism has a certain, perhaps indefinable, but not the less substantial unity, and it is this unit and not its constituent parts or processes that has been the material acted on by evolutionary forces. A physiological process may therefore be expected to lose something of its full natural character when it is isolated from the complete animal for purposes of experimental study. This consideration does in fact express one of the limitations of experimental physiology, and one that is apt to become increasingly manifest in the most advanced branches of the subject. On the whole, however, it is highly remarkable with what success the physiologist has been able to defy this limitation and to detach bodily processes into circumstances of such simplification, or such complete specification, as to make study fruitful without unduly distorting their natural character. Such classical simplifications as the nerve-muscle preparation, the isolated heart, the spinal animal, have been justified beyond all question by the substantial additions to knowledge that have been made through them. These preparations cannot, however, fail to remind us sharply of the difference in the status of experiment in physiology and in physics and chemistry. The essence of a scientific experiment is the specification of its conditions. Now the normal medium of any bodily organ or process is the intact living animal, and its normal activity is closely compounded with that of the whole organism. In drawing conclusions from the behaviour of a physiological preparation it is necessary, therefore, to specify how far it has been modified by being isolated. The difficulty of doing this with fullness and precision is not inconsiderable—even the necessity for it is not always closely attended to—and does undoubtedly counterbalance to some extent the advantages of simplification that the experimental method possesses. When this lack of specification is least surmountable we can see in physiology a tendency to become a science of collateral rather than of direct experiment.

Scientific Method in Human Biology

The distribution of method in the sciences not concerned with the life of man is relatively simple, because all the larger deciding factors are entirely beyond human influence or control. With the sciences of human life,[1] the situation is complicated by the prejudice and the ethical limitations to which direct experiment in man is subject. The effect of these circumstances has been to make the study of the processes of the human body in health and disease dependent chiefly on observation in man combined with experiment in animals. Experiment in animals has had great success in solving the problems of human biology, and has provided one of the most complete proofs of the value of experimental science and of the general similarity of the fundamental vital processes in all animals. At the same time, however, it must be recognized that these experiments have in the strict sense and in relation to man collateral rather than direct validity.

[1] The interrelation of physiology and pathology is so close that from the point of view of method they may be usefully regarded as continuous and inseparable. The apparent necessity for the medical student to complete his knowledge of the normal before beginning his study of the abnormal is probably as fallacious as it is practically wasteful and inconvenient.

The Application of Animal Experiment to Man

The success of animal experiment in human physiology and pathology has been so great and continuous that there has never been any serious call for its collateral quality to be dwelt upon. With the increase of knowledge, however, and the need for a finer and finer penetration into the processes of health and disease, the usefulness of a closer critical examination of the actual state of affairs will probably become manifest. To those whose work in human biology lies in the observational study of man rather than in animal experimentation the value of such an examination tends constantly to present itself. The gap between man and any other animal is large even when judged on the crude basis of manifest structure. When the relation of man to animals is regarded from the functional point of view the gap is seen to be larger and much more significant. It may be useful to specify some of the biological anomalies in the situation of man which cannot be safely ignored in applying experimental results obtained in animals.

The Upright Posture. The simplest case in which the conditions common to most other animals have been drastically rearranged in man is the upright posture. The essential mechanics of the skeleton and of the circulation were established, and as it were tried out, in quadrupedal forms through an enormously long space of time. Upon this well-proved arrangement, and it would seem rather suddenly and without a fundamental mechanical reorganization, was imposed a posture which threw on the old scheme fresh strains that have tried it to within reach of the actual margin of safety. The results of this late and, so to say, hurried revision of the structural plan show themselves far and wide in the pathological field. It is not unreasonable to see these strains as important factors in the so-called static deformities, and in the excessive liability of the lower limbs to diseases of the bones and joints and to circulatory disorders on both the arterial and venous sides. Echoes of the same disturbing element are perhaps to be found in abdominal pathology, and even in the peculiarities of the cerebral circulation. In general, however, it is perhaps in relation to the special qualities of the circulation as a whole in man that the upright posture should arouse the most caution in applying the results of animal experiment.

Longevity. The fact that in man survival to an age long past that of reproduction is a common event makes his general biological position in some ways unique. Morbid states that show themselves on the whole only when reproductive activity is normally waning or at an end can have no selective elimination acting against them; they can thus flourish untouched by what is probably the strongest of all checks upon diseases that normally have their range in or before the active period of sexual life. It seems reasonable to suppose that an essential factor in the inveteracy of cancer and its excessive frequency in man is its existence in what we may call a biological backwater, where it has no effects of selection to contend with. The difference in frequency of sarcoma and carcinoma might perhaps plausibly be accounted for in the same way. In applying the results of animal experiment to pathological conditions in man it seems likely that this peculiar feature in the situation of the latter may be a cause of difficulty, and perhaps of wrong conclusions.

The Effects of Unrestricted Food-supply. It is well recognized that normally, and in a general way, the inclination for food is directly related to emptiness of

the stomach rather than to the nutritional needs of the
animal concerned. The usefulness of this arrangement
is obvious: if the impulse to seek food were felt only
when the body was in need of it to carry on its functions,
there would be a risk that the animal would already have
lost the energy necessary for the search. The normal
animal eats, then, because the stomach is calling for food.
not because the body is calling for nourishment, and the
physiological situation is satisfactory as long as the food
is of low nutritive value, as in the herbivora, or has to
be worked hard for, as with the carnivora. Civilized
man has broken through the natural safeguards of the
process by obtaining a food-supply unlimited both in
nutritive value and in amount, but he still regulates his
eating by the demands of his stomach rather than by the
needs of his body. The result is that by the time middle-
age is reached the absence of some degree of adiposity
is statistically abnormal, and may well give rise to a
suspicion of disease. Here again we find a gross functional discrepancy between man and animals which may
well have a confusing effect in the application of experimental results.

The Effects of Personality. The living animal is a
functional unit dependent on the close correlation and
harmonious working of its parts. There is no reason to
suppose that there is any less essential need for harmony
among its mental activities and between them and its
bodily activities than there is for harmony in the bodily
sphere itself. In animals other than man disharmonies
within the mind or between mind and body, though they
sometimes give hints of their presence, are generally
inconspicuous. The relatively enormous development
of mental activities in man has enlarged correspondingly
the region in which a lack of harmonious working may

arise. Disharmonious mental states, such as those due to the clash of individual and social needs, are notoriously apt to interfere with bodily function to a degree and with a duration and constancy that may simulate organic disease and perhaps initiate it. It is a fact unfortunately beyond contest that, though the interaction of mind and body presents problems to the importance of which lip-service has been abundantly paid, these problems have never received thorough realistic and scientific treatment. The explanation of this deficiency may be in the consideration with which we are here specially concerned, that this is a region in which the functional gap between man and other animals is at its widest and most profound.

The Function of Observation in Human Biology

We have pointed to some of the corrections which may have to be applied to animal experiment before its significance for man can be established. There is, however, another limitation of the range of collateral experiment in human biology. This is in regard to investigations in which access to the subjective side of experience is indispensable. The relation between cerebral states and states of consciousness in the normal and abnormal, and the physiology and pathology of pain, present problems of this class. All these considerations taken together, while they can, of course, in no way depreciate the inestimable gifts human biology has got, and will probably continue to get, from collateral experiment, yet do suggest that for the finest and deepest insight into the most characteristic phenomena of man's life it will be necessary to use, with all its inherent restrictions, the method of direct experiment in man himself.

Our knowledge of normal physiology in man, such as it is, is almost wholly due to the experimental method. In the study of disease, on the other hand, while the experimental method has been very valuable, and promises to be increasingly so, it is to be noted that the method of observation has behind it a long and honourable history; but it cannot be denied that for a considerable time essential progress in our knowledge of disease has come less and less from the time-honoured method of observation and more and more from experiment. Moreover, with all its opportunities, observation has at its best been able to disclose but little of the fundamental processes of disease, of the exact meaning of morbid phenomena, of the precise mechanism lying behind symptoms; whereas experiment has a remarkable series of successes of these very kinds already to its credit. In view of such considerations as these it may well be asked whether the time has not come when it should be recognized, with all the practical consequences that would follow, that observation can no longer be regarded as able to effect serious advances in medicine.

The method of experiment studies phenomena under the simplified and specified conditions of the laboratory; the method of observation studies phenomena as they are presented in the random order of natural events. The first tends to yield clear results capable of analysis by further experimentation; the second tends to yield broader, vaguer conclusions, and its power of penetration by analysis is usually limited. The first requires patience, caution, ingenuity; the second, insight, great familiarity with its material, and what we may call the intuition of reality—that is to say, the power to choose among equally plausible hypotheses the one that best fits the general behaviour of the material in question.

In a very broad way it may be said that successful observation depends more directly on a special mental aptitude than does successful experiment.

The chief limitation in practice on the value of even the best kind of observation is the difficulty in proving its conclusions and therefore of making them available to the general body of science. We have said that successful observation is dependent on special aptitude, and it is notorious that ten experiences will yield a great deal more to one man than a hundred of the same kind to another. This, of course, means that there must usually be a large intuitional element in the conclusions of the able observer, who is apt to be impatient of the drudgery of scientific proof, correspondingly careless in attempting it, and therefore little apt to advance substantially the scientific structure of his subject. The evolution of medicine, which has been so largely dependent on it, illustrates in a peculiarly pointed way the disadvantages to which purely observational inquiry is subject. The method failed to penetrate the nature of infective processes on the one hand, and on the other it ascribed, and indeed still ascribes, a wholly undue importance to insignificant climatic conditions as direct causes of disease. It has held the key to the pathology of vitamin deficiency, to endocrine disorders, to the relation of malaria and mosquito, but has lacked the power decisively to enter into and exploit these new provinces. It has had for the most part to leave unelucidated the events that connect the processes of disease with the symptoms they produce, so that even to-day, for example, pain, which is by far the commonest of all symptoms, is the bugbear of diagnosis and treatment.

The essential feature of the observational method is the recognition of groups of events of which the items are significantly related to one another. The simplest case in the detection of such significant relations is when the suspected series recur in the same order often enough to be easily noticeable. The study of disturbed function in the human body when it has passed beyond its most elementary stages does not, however, provide many sequences that by their invariable recurrence and un- mistakable identity show that their items are inter- related. The total body of phenomena accompanying disturbance of function is very large and very variable, so that the significant series which is being looked for may present itself in a different disguise of detail at each reappearance. The simple method of establishing the significance of a group of phenomena by the dry statisti- cal record of its invariable recurrence in given circum- stances is thus not widely applicable in medicine, and the method of observation has not usually obtained its more considerable advances in this way. More often the ob- server has to be content with a limited number of recur- rences of the group of phenomena, and relies upon his close familiarity with and 'feeling' for his material to confirm the relation he suspects between items of the group. This ability to detect significant relations among apparently unrelated phenomena by a kind of direct examination is the distinguishing gift of the able ob- server.

Observational inquiry then in such a field, for example, as clinical medicine may give results that are question- able on the one hand because too much value has been given to conclusions essentially based on intuition, and on the other hand because the possibilities of exact ob- servation and record have been exaggerated. We are all familiar with instances of large and imposing masses of records vitiated at their very base by the preconceptions of their compilers or by the impossibility of precise record, and with instances of the hieratic pronouncement that rises superior to the need of proof. Neither of these misuses of the method, however, can justify us in ignoring what has been done by it for medicine in the past or in concluding that the period of its usefulness is at an end.

Before inquiring what function the method of observation may yet be able to serve it is well to bring to mind how little the medical sciences can afford to dispense with any means of inquiry that is not demonstrably and wholly sterile. The success of the experimental method has been so great that it has become almost a fixed convention for any general comment on the course of science to deal almost wholly with the triumphs that have been attained by this method and but little with the tasks that have proved too hard for it. This not unamiable weakness is perhaps partly to be explained and excused, at any rate as far as this country is concerned, by the constant hostile pressure against animal experiment and the consequent supposed need to justify it in season and out of season. If, however, we free ourselves, as we may well do for a moment in so technical a discussion as this, from propagandist optimism we shall very easily see that in the interests of science itself we should spare some attention from the triumphs that light up the past, for the needs that darken the future. The progress of science, when regarded with a due realism, is seen always to have been sporadic, to have been subject to lapses of inspiration, to have gone forward in one part of the field at the apparent expense of slackening effort in another. No better illustration of this irregularity in the line of progress could be found than in the fact that after over half a century of experimental pathology the four great scourges of man in temperate climates—influenza, the common cold, cancer, and rheumatism—remain pathological problems so largely unsolved. In the face of a fact like this it is plain that medicine cannot afford to leave unused any implement, however imperfect—especially, perhaps, one to which a definite function otherwise unfulfilled can be assigned.

In trying to define the field in which observation seems to have its characteristic use it is of advantage to get a clear idea of what actually are the chief defects and limitations inherent in the method. Two of these are of such predominant importance that they need only be mentioned: first, the limitation of the extent to which observation can be used in following a problem through stage after stage of elucidation until a fundamental solution is found; and secondly, the readiness with which the method lends itself to faulty or even wholly fallacious conclusions. It may be thought that neither of these defects needs discussion, but perhaps the second has implications which are not always fully realized and which may repay some examination.

Observation and the 'post hoc' Fallacy

The characteristic defect of the observational method as commonly used in medicine is its liability to the *post hoc, propter hoc* fallacy. The only means we possess of establishing a causal relation between events is to observe their invariable occurrence in association. The clinical observer cannot bring about at will the recurrence of events he wishes to study or strip them of irrelevant circumstances as can the experimenter. Moreover, his observations are necessarily made under the pressure of the fact that the events he looks for are not primarily material for science but primarily somebody's symptoms and the signals of somebody's need for help. This urgency in the very air of all clinical work does undoubtedly tend towards the finding of significant relations in sequences of events which longer and more thorough observation would have shown to be unrelated. The well-equipped clinician must possess the qualities of the artist, the man of science, and the humanist, but he must exercise them only in so far as they subserve the getting well of the individual patient. It is a hard doctrine but none the less true that this essential function of the doctor—the care of the given patient—may involve the forgoing of exactly scientific diagnosis, of the artistic perfecting of an operation, or even of the interests of society at large. It is therefore obvious that the influences against the making of scientific observations by those in the actual practice of medicine are very strong; and it is not surprising that the experimenter is apt to find the clinician on the one hand prolific of unsound conclusions and on the other timid and sceptical in applying the results attained in the laboratory by experiment. No better illustration could be found of the characteristic weakness of clinical methods than the extent to which the ascription of disease to trivial climatic discomforts is still accepted or at least tolerated. Colds and phenomena of the order of draughts and wet feet—alleged causes of colds—are sufficiently common to afford ample opportunities for the discovery of insignificant sequences. This fact, together with the psychological influences tending to associate healthy with comfortable conditions, has produced a veritable folklore pathology of colds and chills which true scientific observation would speedily explode, and which presents clinical medicine in one of its least edifying aspects. There are, however, probably even deeper roots of the inveteracy of the *post hoc* fallacy in medicine. If two events A and B occur repeatedly in the same order, experience teaches us to regard them as having the relation of cause and effect—that is to say, of being so related that whenever A appears it will be followed by B, and wherever B is observed it will be found to have been preceded by A. To establish this relation with any great degree of probability the observed recurrences of A and B in that order must be numerous, must be without exception, and the identity of A and B in each observation must be clear. In clinical observation these requirements cannot usually be satisfied with unambiguous severity; the able observer, therefore, while constantly trying to satisfy them as far as the case permits, will depend more or less on the insight and sense of reality that his familiarity with his material and his natural aptitude have given him.

It is notorious that a conviction of the existence of a causal relationship between two events—a very different thing from the objective proof of such a relationship—is far from being dependent on such deliberate and cautious procedures. In everyday affairs, and to a certain extent in the general run of clinical work, the number of accepted causal relationships far exceeds the number of demonstrated and even of probable cases. It seems likely, then, that there is some strong natural tendency which inclines us to ascribe causal relations to events accidentally and arbitrarily occurring near one another. That we have such a tendency is at least suggested by the work of Pavlov on conditioned reflexes. The essential facts of this work are familiar and need not be recalled in detail. In a dog, in which a salivary fistula has been established so that the flow of saliva can be measured, the presentation of food is followed at once by a profuse secretion. Some arbitrarily chosen stimulus such as the sounding of a metronome is now made to precede immediately the offer of food. After this sequence has been repeated a few times it is found that the auditory stimulus causes a similar salivary flow without any presentation of food. The cerebral cortex has been taught by a very short experience to accept the metronome sound as a precursor of food. In mental terms the sound has become a 'cause' of food, and an intelligent dog might classify metronomes in the group of things to be hunted like rats and rabbits. The facts especially to be noted for our purpose here are: first, the readiness with which the link of apparent causation has been formed; secondly, the arbitrariness of the sequence, metronomes having no relation with food in the general objective world; and thirdly, the fact that the relation can be fixed only by adding it to a relation already established—namely, a natural reflex—in this case the visual-salivary reflex.

Enough has been said earlier in this paper to enjoin caution in applying the results of experiments in animals to man. Caution must, moreover, be especially stringent in seeking light on mental problems from cerebral phenomena. Nevertheless, it is clear enough that there is a remarkably close analogy between the aptitude for the formation of conditioned reflexes on the one hand and on the other hand the tendency too readily to ascribe the causal relation to small and unrelated sequences of events; and we may at least suspect that the subjective sense of causation we so easily derive from a few random coincidences is connected with the proved capacity of the brain to pick up arbitrary and as it were 'irrational' reflexes. The conditioned reflex then is perhaps the simplest case of the *post hoc* fallacy. When we thus see reason to suspect that our tendency to impute causal relations unjustifiably may be the expression of a characteristic cerebral function we need not be surprised that this fallacy is so common and so difficult to avoid.

We are now in a position to review shortly the disadvantages of the observational method in the study of medical problems as we see it in actual use. These disadvantages fall into three groups.

1. The method as an instrument of inquiry is of limited range. In the systematic attack on a given problem carried on stage by stage until a solution is reached it is notably weak compared with the experimental method to which, in this function, it must always and of necessity remain grossly inferior.

2. The method is known as a matter of experience to be especially open to the *post hoc* fallacy. Though this may not be fundamental and essential as is the limitation noted above, we have seen that there may be an organic predisposition underlying it.

3. In clinical medicine the difficulties of securing objective proof by exact observation of identically recurrent events are very great. This tends to make the observer rely on intuition rather than on established conclusions and to make him impatient of the labour of proving or disproving the truth of opinions arrived at by intuition. The result is that the current clinical medicine of any given period is apt to be loaded with 'authoritative' opinions often contradictory of one another, many of which are actually capable of, but have never been submitted to, definite proof or disproof.

Limitations of the Experimental Method

Experiment is observation made in specifiable and controllable circumstances and it seeks to eliminate that dependence on the personal judgement, the tact, the intuition of the observer which is the weakness of the observational method. If we imagine a problem to be attacked and solved independently by experiment and by observation, the solution by the latter method, in addition to having taken longer and being less exact, will generally have demanded a more arduous and intricate intellectual exercise than the solution by the former.

This economy of experiment in its demands upon certain of the less definable aptitudes of the mind is no doubt a contributory cause of its great success as a method, but probably it has secondary consequences which in the long run and on the large scale are not wholly advantageous. A science which is strictly limited to the experimental method is apt to favour in its workers a tendency to deprecate any great speculative activity and to regard an interest in the free play of ideas for their own sake as evidence of a lack of scientific stability and trustworthiness. Such a distrust of the intellect involves an unsound view of the function of ideas in science. It is a mistake to suppose, as it is so easy to do, that science enjoins upon us the view that any given idea is true or false and there is an end of it; an idea may be neither demonstrably true nor false and yet be useful, interesting, and good exercise. Again, it is poverty rather than fertility of ideas that causes them to be used as a substitute for experiment, to be fought for with prejudice or decried with passion. When ideas are freely current they keep science fresh and living and are in no danger of ceasing to be the nimble and trusty servants of truth. We may perhaps allow ourselves to say that the body of science gets from the steady work of experiment and observation its proteins, its carbohydrates, and—sometimes too profusely—its fats, but that without its due modicum of the vitamin of ideas the whole organism is apt to become stunted and deformed, and above all to lose its resistance to the infection of orthodoxy.

The state of inorganic chemistry in the early nineties of the last century showed some traces of the conditions which too exclusive a reverence for experiment is apt to bring about. The inspiration of the atomic idea was manifestly dying, yet any whisper that the atom might not be the ultimate unit of reality was apt to be snubbed as speculative and unscientific. Nevertheless this impeccable science could tolerate for many years a discrepancy of the order of 1 per cent. in the results of the different methods of preparing nitrogen, and with all its faith in experiment could ascribe the discrepancy to experimental error. And all the while, behind the meagre veil of this experimental error the inert gases of the air were impatiently awaiting discovery. The agitated scepticism with which the discovery of argon was received, no less than the great growth of which that discovery was the germ, illustrated how much chemistry had for the moment lost the aptitude for new ideas and the elasticity of mind which their currency produces. Physiology, though in a less extreme degree, has illustrated from time to time the periodical languor to which a purely experimental science is subject in the absence of the stimulation of ideas from without. Fortunately, its inevitably close, though perhaps not very highly prized, relation to medicine has repeatedly given it the stimulus necessary for renewed vitality, as, for example, in the case of the idea of cerebral localization and the idea of internal secretion. With such illustrations in mind it may perhaps be admitted that experimental science does not of itself and of necessity produce the most useful attitude towards ideas.

It is sometimes taken as a matter of course that scepticism is the very highest flower of the scientific spirit. The thesis might be admitted to have an aspect of truth if it did not so often cover a mere automatic means of protecting ourselves against the painful irruption of new ideas. If the reader of this paper will ask himself what has been his attitude towards anything in it that may have been new to him, he will probably find that his reaction has been far less to explore what possibilities the unfamiliar idea may have happened to possess, than almost automatically and at first sight to look for arguments against it. And if he were challenged to give the reasons for his matter-of-course use of this method he would no doubt defend it as essentially scientific.

Even if it is admitted that opposition towards ideas is an attitude of mind not best calculated to extract what value they may contain, we are apt to be told that the true scientific position is that of the famous 'suspense of judgement'. It cannot, however, be conceded that even this time-honoured phrase represents an attitude quite free of the defensive taint. The truly scientific mind is altogether unafraid of the new, and while having no mercy for ideas which have served their turn or shown their uselessness, it will not grudge to any unfamiliar conception its moment of full and friendly attention, hoping to expand rather than to minimize what small core of usefulness it may happen to contain. It is this capacity in scientific workers for what we may call provisional acceptance that encourages in science the steady flow of ideas and tends to preserve it from those periods of intellectual languor to which, as we have seen, the purely experimental sciences seem in some degree to be prone.

We have shown that observational study is subject to certain defects, especially in its liability to fallacy and its limitations as an exact instrument. But when it is successfully practised it renders necessary the special cultivation of certain qualities of mind—intuition, imagination, the feeling for reality—which are just those which may be expected to provide that flow of ideas that keep the study of a science animated and interesting. It would seem, therefore, that it must be an advantage to an experimental science to have an observational side, the function of which, in addition to its use as an implement of research, would chiefly be to promote the atmosphere of intellectual liveliness which is so important an evidence of health.

If these considerations are sound they afford good reason to think that our desire to forward the scientific study of medicine and the branches of knowledge on which medicine depends will be best fulfilled not only by promoting the use of experiment wherever possible and by bringing every problem that admits of it to an experimental test, but also by keeping alive the method of observation in medical studies and doing what we can to give it the benefit of scientific principles of use. In order that observation should have its proper value certain principles we have already indicated must be thoroughly familiar. The true nature of the method must be understood, its special liabilities to fallacy must be known, and its weakness of trusting to intuition when actual proof is possible, overcome. There can be little doubt that it is this last-named characteristic of ordinary clinical practice that inclines the critics of the observational method in medicine to view it with so little charity or hope. In clinical work proof is usually difficult to obtain, often tedious and unencouraging to attempt, and not rarely altogether impossible; at the same time any effort towards it is constantly overshadowed by the urgency to act. It is natural, therefore, for the expert clinician to rely on his intuition and judgement even when actual and final proof is possible, though this preference does constitute a reproach to the method from any scientific point of view. If clinical observation is to renew its prestige and to continue its indispensable function of stimulating the experimental attack on medical problems, it can do so by showing resolution in looking for proof wherever proof is possible, and a scientific standard in its scrutiny of evidence.

Conclusion

In reviewing the principles of method by which the task of the medical sciences is to be carried forward we have seen reason to group the resources available into three classes: first, experiment with animals; secondly, experiment with man; and, thirdly, clinical observation. All of these methods are necessary for sound and continuous progress, but each has its special province, and each has certain limitations which prevent its being wholly independent of the others.

1. *Animal experiment*, which we have ventured to call collateral experiment, must always be the chief instrument for the solution of fundamental medical problems. It has to be recognized, however, that the functional gap between man and other animals, and especially those commonly available in laboratories, is larger even than the morphological gap. We have pointed out four of the regions in which this discrepancy is largest, and where, therefore, special caution is necessary in applying animal results to man. The need for such caution is, however, fundamental and general, if medicine is to get

the fullest benefit from what has been, and still is, its most fruitful resource.

2. *Experiment in man*, or direct experiment, limited in possibilities of application as it necessarily must be, is the one wholly unexceptionable method available for the solution of problems of human health and disease. Though its history is still very short, it has already proved remarkably fruitful. There can be no doubt that one of the chief duties before medicine at present is the exploitation of the method of direct experiment. The natural history of sciences, however, seems to indicate that a diet of pure experimentation in a limited field is not enough for permanent scientific health. If experimental medicine is to progress healthily it must have a full supply of ideas, and must know how to deal with them. Such a purpose can best be served by a close contact with the realities of clinical medicine.

3. *Clinical observation* has given to medicine very long and very honourable service. There is a certain melancholy in recognizing, as we must, that it has never been, except in the hands of an occasional genius, a very effective instrument for penetrating the fundamental secrets of health and disease, and in recognizing that we now possess far more effective instruments for this purpose. To recognize these facts is, however, by no means to acquiesce in the view that clinical observation has no longer important functions to fulfil in progressive medicine. In the first place it is still a valuable method of scientific research. At the same time it must be admitted that the method is, in some respects, far less general and far less simple than that of experiment; that it lends itself to the solution of only a limited class of problems, and that it demands, at any rate for its great strokes, a somewhat special aptitude of mind. Moreover, if it is to make

itself less dependent on special aptitude, a wider interest in the need for and the means of proving its propositions will be necessary. It is possible that the increasing knowledge of experimental methods may bring this about and stimulate a renewed vigour in purely clinical work. In the second place, as successful clinical observation demands a certain special aptitude, and the unresting contemplation of a very large and rich material such as we find at its highest in, for example, a Hughlings Jackson, it should be the source and reservoir of that flow of ideas which alone can maintain the fertility of the whole field of medical science.

To the experimenter immersed in his research, and to the clinician struggling with the load of experience and the needs of his patients, it may seem unpractical to concern ourselves with the theory of medical knowledge. On the other hand, it is perhaps the lack of rational doctrine and a general interest in the problems of method that has made medicine the scene of so much disunited and contradictory effort, and helped to put it down from its historical position as the mother and the nurse of science.

DE MINIMIS[1]

I

THE familiar saying from which I have taken my title and my text tells us that the law does not concern itself with very small matters—*de minimis non curat lex*. If this aphorism gives an authentic glimpse of the legal mind, it tells us also that that enigmatic organ differs sharply in at least one particular from the mind of science. For it is characteristic of science not to value things by their size or according to their apparent importance in the eye of common sense. The scientific world is a democracy of facts where the inhabitants are of equal standing and there is no table of precedence. Indeed, the progress of knowledge has been in great part the discovery of the importance of small things and the exaltation of the insignificant. The great development of the medical sciences in the last sixty years has got most of its strength from such a continued revelation of the minute. At its beginning was the demonstration of the meaning of bacteria in disease, about its middle the discovery of the vitamins, in its recent stages the study of the viruses. All these have been concerned with things or substances of which the effective action has been in spite of sizes or amounts excessively small. The theory of microbic disease displaced supposed causes of what we may call naked-eye size—cold and wet, damps, miasmas, and infected airs. For them it substituted bodies at that time almost inconceivably small—the veritable minims of nature. I use that term 'minims of nature' to express the smallest imaginable dose of life,

[1] Delivered before the Guild of Public Pharmacists on 18 Jan. 1933. Reprinted from the *Lancet*, 11 Feb. 1933, p. 287.

K

not only because in that sense it has good authority behind it—no less, for example, than that of John Milton —but because in this company it must come to our ears with a homely sound. Perhaps we may regret that the pioneers of bacteriology did not revive it instead of inventing in 1878 the term microbe out of misused Greek. If they had been content with established English a pleasant link would have been left between the language of pharmacy and that of pathology. We might well also have been grateful to be able to speak of the viruses as 'minims of nature' when we learn that there are among them living particulate and formidable agents so small as to surpass by little the individual *molecules* of haemoglobin.

The theory of deficiency disease introduced to pathology a principle as wholly new as did the microbe. Like that it involved an immense change of scale and the demonstration that what might be called the naked-eye view of the constituents of the living body was inadequate. But the new principle was of a different kind from that necessary to found bacteriology. No pursuit of the old climatic and sanitarian theories of disease with whatever thoroughness could have led to the doctrine of microbic pathology without the revolutionary inquiries of Pasteur which disclosed an unsuspected mode of existence. On the other hand dietetics failed to disclose the vitamins because inquiries had not been exact and exhaustive enough. The problem of the vitamins was in fact a residuary problem. The dietetic field had been harvested and even gleaned except for what seemed a few inconspicuous remnants that for a long time it was agreed to ignore. Yet it was these very residues that were to yield the richest harvest of all. This peculiarity makes the solution of the vitamin problem of special

interest to the student of scientific method. It is therefore as the leading recent case of a problem of the
residuary type that I have reminded you of it, for I propose to call your attention in some little detail to that
class of problem and its significance for the theory of
method.

The economic value of working-over rejected residues
has often been proved by the mining engineer and the
metallurgist; similarly the need for vigilance in securing
complete exhaustion of raw materials has shown its value
to the chemist and the pharmacist. These lessons may
usefully serve as metaphorical injunctions in the prosecu-
tion of scientific research itself. Time after time it has
been shown in the latter activity that the humblest residual phenomena have concealed great secrets. In order
to give this point all the salience I can, I shall go outside
the field of medicine, and even of the biological sciences,
to that of inorganic chemistry, and shall venture to recall to you the familiar and even hackneyed story of the
finding of argon and the other inert gases of the air.

II

In the last quarter of the eighteenth century the
study of the elementary gases was being pursued in
England with much activity. Among those who were
thus engaged we chiefly remember to-day the names of
Priestley, Watt, Black, and Cavendish. Of these, Henry
Cavendish was perhaps the ablest investigator as he was
certainly the most extraordinary man. He was a mil-
lionaire and the grandson of a duke; yet his mode of life
was hermit-like and spartan, his manner shy to the
extent of oddity, and though he was a great experimenter, the publication of his researches was notably
careless and hesitating. This last characteristic left his

reputation for long far below his merits, but to give a measure of his real quality we need only recall that he was the first to demonstrate the constitution of water by hydrogen and oxygen and its synthesis from those elements.

Sometime before 1785 Cavendish was studying the separation of nitrogen from the air. He used the method of passing a stream of electric sparks through a glass tube containing air mixed with excess of oxygen. The nitrogen and oxygen combined to form an oxide of nitrogen which was absorbed by a solution of caustic potash, while the oxygen was removed by another absorbent. When, therefore, the process was complete and all the nitrogen oxidized, his tube should have been empty of any gas. But the result was different and I will quote his description of it, using, however, the modern terms for the gas concerned. After these processes he says, 'a small bubble of air remained unabsorbed which was certainly not more than 1/120 of the [nitrogen] let up the tube. So that if there is any part of the [nitrogen] of our atmosphere which differs from the rest and cannot be reduced to nitrous acid we may safely conclude that it is not more than 1/120 part of the whole'. That bubble, of course, was argon. Cavendish had seen it, but argon remained undiscovered. If curiosity was aroused at any time during the next century by this ambiguous residue in Cavendish's eudiometer, it has left no record; and we may be sure that any questionings were invariably stilled by the comfortable assumption of experimental error.

III

It was over a hundred years later, in the last decade of the nineteenth century, that the meaning of this residue was explained, but the residue itself had first to be rediscovered by a wholly different line of approach. Chiefly owing to the work of Cavendish and his contemporaries, inorganic chemistry had experienced a continuous and successful development; but it had now fallen, as those of us who were students then can remember, on rather hard times. It had reached one of the flat periods to which all purely experimental sciences seem to be subject. The inspiration derived from its founders, after burning brilliantly for so long, was dying down. Ideas were few and—an even more ominous sign—were apt when they were at all speculative to be deprecated in the name of science. This dread of speculation, and the disguise of it as scientific austerity, are characteristic symptoms shown by an experimental science when its life is running thin. Such phenomena were, for example, apt to appear in the discussion of one of the few speculative conceptions that had found any kind of currency among chemists—the once famous 'Prout's hypothesis'. William Prout, it may be of interest to recall here, was a doctor as well as a chemist, and the discoverer of the presence of free hydrochloric acid in the gastric juice. As early as 1815 he enunciated the view that there must be a simple numerical relation between the atomic weights of hydrogen and the other elements, and that hydrogen was a sort of elementary substance that in some way entered into the composition of the others. Even on the evidence then to be reckoned with, this was a sensible and not very recondite guess, but in the next seventy or eighty years it produced from time to time a surprising amount of indignant criticism. It must of course be admitted that to those who had comfortably settled down to the view that each element is made up of irreducible indivisible billiard balls of a special kind, it was an irritating and repulsive dose. By them it was naturally criticized as a flighty departure from scientific rectitude, and I can remember the feeling some of my teachers gave me that it was a little disreputable even to entertain such an idea. Yet it was true; and it gave the hint that was to begin an energetic revival and extension of inorganic chemistry.

The hint was taken by a man whose personality (fortunately preserved for us by his son in a notably graphic memoir) would in itself justify the recall of the events that ensued. The third Lord Rayleigh was born into a family of country squires and landowners, and in many respects was thoroughly representative of his class. He was as strong a Conservative, as sound a church-goer, and as firm an upholder of the established order as his position and convictions demanded. He was brought up among the assumptions of a world which seemed to itself endowed and established for ever, and which is still indestructibly preserved for us in the annals of Middlemarch and Barchester. The main physical circumstance of his youth was the profound security of rural England, where the mild landscape and the deeply rooted village looked humbly to the Great House standing side by side with the church. Experience shows that a type and an environment such as this are not among the richer sources of our scientific masters. But they permitted Rayleigh, as they had permitted Henry Cavendish, to become one of the leading physical investigators of his day; and they perhaps reinforced, in the case of Rayleigh, the caution, the patience, and the stable judgement in which he conspicuously excelled.

It was these last gifts that were to be of decisive value when in 1882 he yielded, as many physicists had done before, to the siren song of Prout's hypothesis, and made up his mind to decide once for all whether, if every precaution that even his patience could suggest were taken, it might not be possible to show that a simple arithmetical relation did obtain between the atomic weight of hydrogen and those of the other elementary gases. This involved the weighing of these gases under exact conditions, and was of course an enormously laborious task. After some years the work on hydrogen and oxygen was completed, but though it failed to bring the atomic weight of the latter nearer to the hoped for 16 than 15.882, we find him in 1892 at work on nitrogen which had promised to be technically a less arduous affair. Things went well with this, and he was comparatively soon in possession of a stable weight for the gas that satisfied his exacting standards. He might well have supposed his task was done, but in fact he was innocently approaching its crisis. He had been weighing nitrogen got from air and therefore, as we now know, mixed with the heavier argon. This would be discovered only if the weight obtained were compared with the weight of nitrogen got from chemical decomposition and therefore free from argon. He stood thus at the parting of two courses of infinitely different significance. A good and consistent series of weights had been obtained; any man might have been satisfied with such a result. Down that road lay a moderate satisfaction and relief from a long and inexpressibly tedious research, but nothing else. He might, on the other hand, decide that he must confirm his results by work on nitrogen got from another source than air. Down that road, all unsuspected, lay heavy labours and anxieties, but also lay the finding of argon and consequences beyond any dream. There cannot have been many more critical moments in the history of science.

IV

It is a natural impulse of historians to make a good deal of what are called the turning points of history. At these nodes in the story of the past there is apt to be a concentration of issues on a single hour or on a single man, an intensification of meaning that gives dignity even to the trivial, a heightened illusion of free will in the actors. All these combine to endow the vague historic plungings of mankind with an air of design and aesthetic structure, so that it is but a poor historian who does not make an effective scene of Caesar at the Rubicon, or Charles Edward at Derby. The history of knowledge has not been much recognized as yielding moments of an equal intensity, perhaps because its high occasions are undecorated by trumpet or banner and call to mind no sound of marching feet. But to the ear in tune with the finer vibrations of reality, science has had its crises which give a not less authentic thrill, and here was one of them. We watch Rayleigh at this turning-point in the history of science with a confidence that is derived from our knowledge of his character as much as from our knowledge of the sequel. His caution and patience and judgement now had their unique opportunity. He decided that nitrogen prepared from chemical combination must also be weighed to confirm the weight obtained from atmospheric nitrogen, and he was soon brought up against a clear and unshakable discrepancy between the two results; the chemical nitrogen was $\frac{1}{2}$ per cent. lighter than the atmospheric nitrogen. It is not necessary to follow the steps of the toilsome research by which it was proved that the excess weight of the atmospheric nitrogen was due to mixture with an unknown constituent of the air. At the end it became clear that this unknown gas was the 'small bubble of air' which

had 'remained unabsorbed' in Henry Cavendish's eudiometer, and whose enigmatic presence had stood in the
background of chemistry inviting curiosity in vain for
over a hundred years. It was composed of the inertest
substance in the physical world. In the intellectual world,
however, it produced a veritable series of explosions.
Argon led to helium and neon; helium pointed the way to
the mode of disintegration of the radio-active atom, neon
to isotopes and the meaning of the periodic succession
of the elements. It is therefore no departure from rational
moderation to say that this historic 'bubble of air' was
one of the most pregnant residues in the whole history
of chemical analysis.

Whatever intrinsic interest this old story may possess, I should not have ventured to tell it except as a
classical illustration of the significance of residuary
phenomena in the history of science. That general lesson
must surely provoke us to ask what application of it we
can make in the departments of knowledge with which
we are more specially concerned. I propose, therefore, to
consider briefly certain aspects of medicine to which it
may be relevant.

v

The fundamental activity of medical science is to
determine the ultimate causation of disease. That statement sounds like a complete commonplace and should
be one. We may perhaps, however, feel some doubt
whether we all of us keep it in mind as clearly as we
might. The brilliancy and the practical value of the
great discoveries that have elucidated the processes of
disease tend a little to obscure the fact that many of
them tell us nothing about ultimate causation. Thus we
are apt to speak of the treatment of myxoedema by

thyroid extract or the treatment of diabetes by insulin
as if the primary pathological state were affected by the
remedy instead of being merely compensated for. As a
matter of fact, when we come to survey more attentively
the general state of medical science we cannot but be
struck by the slight extent to which much recent progress—as, for example, that on the relation of internal
secretion to the production of symptoms—has enlightened us in the matter of ultimate causes. A great
deal of this work, though of course of the greatest value,
has been on what we may call the physiological level,
and has scarcely penetrated to fundamental pathology.

It may be interesting to glance over in a summary
way the actual situation as regards our knowledge of the
causation of disease. At present we can enumerate only
six agents:

Injury.	Poisoning.
Malformation.	Parasitic infection.
Defect of diet.	Neoplasm.

Of these it will be noticed that two—malformation and
neoplasm—are not to be regarded as primary in a strict
sense, since in time they will almost certainly be resolved
into other factors. Setting aside, therefore, the pathological phenomena deriving from these two, we may say
that we have for the explanation of the whole of the rest
of disease only four principles—injury, defect of diet,
poisoning, and parasitic infection. Let us now approach
the situation from another aspect. The diseases known
to us fall into three groups: first, those that can be
assigned with certainty to one of the four causes we have
enumerated; secondly, those which have been assigned
with more or less probability to one of these; and thirdly,
those of which the cause is unknown. The rate at which
fresh diseases pass over from the third group to the first,

and are found to be due to one of the known kinds of
cause, is nowadays slow, and tends necessarily, other
things being equal, to become slower. The question
thus inevitably arises whether a time may not come and
how far away it is, when the application of known principles to the explanation of disease will be at a standstill.
Another way of putting the same question would be to
ask how far it is likely that the further extensive explanation of disease depends on the discovery of some totally
new principle comparable with the microbe or the vitamin. Consider such common and serious diseases as
exophthalmic goitre, diabetes, and disseminate sclerosis.
They have been under investigation a long time and
with an increasing refinement of method, yet, however
much we may have learnt of their mechanism, we still
know nothing about their ultimate causation. Are they
likely to be brought under causal mechanisms we already
know, or are they and other diseases in a similar situation, like the residuary 'bubble of air' in Henry Cavendish's eudiometer, awaiting for their explanation some
radical fresh development? In answer to these questions
we cannot make even a plausible guess.

In the last sixty years two wholly new causes of
disease have been discovered—microbic infection and
vitamin deficiency. The first of these explained a group
of diseases which carried a certain broad clinical resemblance, so that a very acute clinician, in the days before
bacteriology, might well have been able to guess that
whatever their causes they were of the same general
order. The case was strikingly different with the diseases
explained by vitamin deficiency. In their clinical mani-
festations these were remarkably miscellaneous, and
showed differences of the widest kind, such as, for
example, those between rickets, beriberi, and scurvy.

No clinician, however alert, could have guessed that these were due to cognate causes. Furthermore, the deficiency diseases seem actually to mimic the diseases caused by other agents; consider, for example, the resemblance between vitamin-B deficiency and alcohol poisoning, each with its acute cerebral symptoms and chronic peripheral neuritis, and the resemblance of scurvy to an infection. The discovery of deficiency diseases has thus disclosed that allied causes may produce clinical effects showing no hint of any kind of relation, and has thus made it more difficult than ever to infer from clinical phenomena any suggestion as to new prime agents of disease.

VI

I should have hesitated to indulge in these extended reflections about residuary phenomena in relation to science in general and medicine in particular, if I had intended to abandon the subject in the complete blind alley into which it seems to have led us. It is true that we can form no reasonable opinion whether the great mass of disease still remaining unexplained will be cleared up by the more thorough exploitation of principles already known to us, or whether its final elucidation will be in any or in great part made by the discovery of some new kind of cause. Engaging as that problem must be to any philosophic student of medicine, it must remain for the present in the region of insoluble conjecture, but its interest may have a useful property if it sends us for some hint of guidance back to the history of science. If we may be allowed to return for a moment to a topic on which we have perhaps already too inordinately dwelt, we shall recall that the discovery of argon was due to Rayleigh's determination to carry the measurement of the known phenomena to a finer point than had yet been reached. In his branch of knowledge the saying that science is measurement was already familiar and manifestly true. As an indirect result of his work the idea can now be carried much farther, and we can say that, at least in the atomic world, all quality is quantity. In such a doctrine we seem to be very far from the biological sciences, and still farther from anything that could ever be recognizably human. Nevertheless it may remind us that the need and use for exact measurement in those sciences have steadily increased and must continue to do so.

Up to the present time medicine has almost wholly avoided the burden of measurement. Its field is so rich and various that qualitative methods of inquiry have proved at least adequate. Signs, however, are beginning to be perceptible that perhaps the main harvest of those methods has been gathered. If these omens are fulfilled, a time will come when an exact and exhaustive numerical exploration of the facts of disease will have to be undertaken. When we contemplate the practical success and the continued progress of medicine we are apt to overlook the fact that it is without precise data. Consider merely the distribution of health and disease in relation to topography, climate, race, sex, and age. Our knowledge of these fundamentals is a series of the vaguest approximations; if we had really exact knowledge of them it is quite probable that many problems of causation now insoluble could be solved by inspection. A similar lack of real exactitude is present in our knowledge of normal functions such as the pulse-rate, temperature, reflexes, sleep, appetite, right-handedness, weight and muscular strength, and above all, in our knowledge of the extent to which these functions are capable of adaptation.

It is obvious that to obtain information of the required precision on matters such as these is altogether beyond the range of the individual worker. Thus our final conclusion must necessarily be that if medicine is to acquire a secure foundation of exact and measured data, it can do so only as the result of inquiries far more widespread and co-ordinated than have yet come within the range of practical contemplation.

The considerations we have surveyed have led us through a course of which the windings may not have shown any very clear relevance to this occasion. Our conclusion, however, could not have been reached in circumstances more appropriate. The only branch of medicine which has always, and with increasing intentness and success, pursued the ideal of exact measurement is pharmacy. I do not think there can be any reasonable doubt that the future of the parent subject to a large extent depends on how far she is able to adopt the characteristic method of her daughter.

GENERAL IDEAS IN MEDICINE[1]

O N 2 August 1775 John Hunter wrote to Edward
Jenner a short letter, which contained what are
perhaps to-day his best-known words. Jenner had asked
for his opinion on a problem of natural history, and
Hunter suggests that the question could be settled ex-
perimentally; and then he breaks out into one of his
brusque, impatient phrases, 'But why think, why not try
the experiment?' In this small outburst the piety of later
times has sometimes seen profundities it might have
surprised its author to be notified of, and has even given
to it the status of an aphorism pregnant with the wisdom
of the newer world. We may incline to regard these
rather high-flown interpretations as belonging to the
sphere of Hunterian Orators, where such tropical growths
naturally bloom. Nevertheless, the phrase on which they
are founded is a text well suited to guide some reflections
on the relation of thought and action in the advancement
of knowledge. Any such discussion must traverse
treacherous ground, and we should therefore not be
afraid of limiting ourselves to elementary considerations
or of defining our terms with care.

In the life story of mankind two implements of knowledge can be plainly seen at work. I have already called
them thought and action, and our first tasks must be to
make clear what is meant by them and to identify some
of the many names by which they may be known. By
action as contrasted with thought I mean man's direct
dealings with phenomena by way of observation and

[1] The Lloyd Roberts Lecture delivered at the House of the Royal Society of
Medicine, 30 Sept. 1935. Reprinted from the *British Medical Journal*, 5 Oct.
1935, vol. ii, p. 609.

experiment, or in the broadest sense of the word, experience. By thought as contrasted with action I mean the rational contemplation of experience and the integration of it into generalized expressions; I shall speak of the use of reason or of the rational mind and of abstract thought as having the same meaning.

It is one of the most curious features in the history of man that his sole uniquely human character, the rational mind, has borne a relation to the advance of knowledge that has always been capricious, often ambiguous, and sometimes hostile. It seems so natural to take it for granted that reason has been the steady friend of truth that a statement of the facts has an air of paradox. If, however, we are to fight shy of the paradoxical, no inquiry into the history of knowledge will take us far. Not less surprising than the enigmatic relation of reason to truth is perhaps the lateness of the date at which it first seems to have occurred to man that the intellect could be deliberately used. Cultures of great vigour and elaboration had climbed to their zenith and died before we get our first glimpse of reason at work on human destiny in the great days of ancient Greece. There we see the rare spectacle of a new and powerful instrument in hands fully competent for its use. The world has come to agree that there never has been anything else quite like the efflorescence produced by the happy union of the Greeks' discovery of abstract thought, and the exulting brilliance with which they applied it. Up to that moment man's only implements for discovery and for preserving its fruits were the practical arts. The characteristic limitations of that method had made him the deferential slave of phenomena; henceforth he was to be in some sense their conscious master. It will be our task to try to get a clear idea of the instrument that could produce this revolution, and then to trace its influence in later times.

The Nature of Abstract Thought

The discovery that we first clearly find in use by the Greeks was that the qualities of objects can be thought of as separable from them. Such abstracted qualities can be recombined and handled within the mind with a facility and fruitfulness impossible in our dealings with actual objects themselves. If complete abstraction of the qualities of the outer world were possible our reconstruction of them in thought would be as valid as the originals, and a true experimental science within the mind would be feasible. It seems probable that the Greeks thought this to be the case, and excusably in the first flush of their discovery. That error has beset the progress of knowledge for two and a half millennia, and compels us to regard the discovery of abstract thought as in some degree a Grecian gift in the old ambiguous sense. For it is a stubborn, though, unfortunately, an elusive, fact that valid abstraction from phenomena in general is only a limited possibility. As far as we know number is the only quality that can be completely abstracted from objects, so that the experience of number within the mind is just as valid as the experience of number attached to external objects, and of course far more easily subject to experiment. Thus the science of number is the single science that is at once fully abstract and fully experimental. The science of spatial relations runs it very close, and it was two thousand years or more before suspicion arose that the abstract space of the mind was not exactly the same thing as space in general. The Greeks were quick to see how well number and space lent themselves to the new method, and very obviously reserved a special reverence for the two corresponding sciences—not always without queer results.

As we move away from number and space abstract thinking becomes less and less able to represent usefully the actual world. In biology the most elaborate abstractions are apt to be mere crude diagrams, and, through disproportionate emphasis, easily pass into caricature. The decline in the effectiveness of abstraction with increase in the multiformity of the phenomena is a familiar fact. The implement so useful to Galileo in attacking mechanics is scarcely recognizable in the hands of Herbert Spencer generalizing biology, even if we grant the powers of the two men to have been equal. It is not, however, the limitations of the method that concern us chiefly here. What is more important in the history of science and of medicine is the tendency of abstract thinking to interpose between the inquirer and the phenomena and to give a diminishing importance to the latter. One universal law has always governed the evolution of knowledge; it is that progress is directly proportional to the closeness of the relation of the inquirer and the facts. Now facts unfortunately are not the natural diet of the mind. They are laborious and often undignified to collect; they are apt to be formless, ugly, and even nasty; they dirty the fingers, they smell, and sometimes bite. How different from the noble, shapely, and above all well behaved, conceptions of the mind, which are so manifestly of a higher order of reality! The fastidious Greeks were very sensitive to this difference and not a little apt to look down on the mere base collection of facts. Even the tremendous Aristotle was not quite untouched by this intellectual queasiness.

REASON ENTHRONED

Faith in the ultimate supremacy of reason must tend towards a dogmatic rationalism. This tendency was not without its ill effects on the pursuit of knowledge by the ancient Greeks, but was to a great extent compensated for by their unique curiosity and aptitude for free thought. It could not keep such a people out of contact with facts, as we see repeatedly throughout the long period from the clinical observations of Hippocrates and the biology of Aristotle down to the experimental physiology of Galen. But when it was handed on to minds less happily situated and less richly endowed, and had been developed into the flawless and invulnerable rationality of the scholastics, rationalism became a much more formidable barrier to the progress of knowledge than it had been as the relatively innocent foible of the Greeks. Medieval rationalism was strong enough to embody in a reasonable structure all known facts. It needed no new ones, and could scarcely have regarded the collection of such as other than foolish and unnecessary.

One of the most deeply enigmatic events in human history is that after the time of Galen science, and with it medicine, underwent no large change but that of decline for a full thousand years. I shall not yield to the temptation to speculate about the causes of this astonishing coma of the human spirit. Many explanations of it have been propounded, and have been for the most part as confident in their presentation as they were incredible in their substance. While bluntly admitting that the fact is unexplained, we may note that in its circumstances there were features that may have been related to it. The most obvious of these was the development of dogmatic rationalism into a system which could give a coherent and consistent account of nature, of man, of the spiritual world, and of any other kind of world that might be supposed to exist. The second and far the more mysterious feature was a lapse of that kind of curiosity for the outer world that makes phenomena interesting in themselves. This is the fundamental impulse of science; without it science is impossible, with it science cannot fail ultimately to appear. Whether or not we may suppose the eclipse of curiosity to have been causally related to the long night of science, it is certain that no dawn could have broken until that eclipse had ended.

The way in which science was born again confirms this principle. It has been shown by Singer that the renaissance of science in the sixteenth century had been prepared for by a long period, during which a reawakened interest in the outer world was gathering momentum. He takes the memorable year 1543, in which were published the masterpieces of Vesalius and Copernicus,[1] as a convenient date to mark the first full light of the scientific renaissance; and he gives evidence of a steadily growing body of work produced in the previous two hundred years that proves interest in external phenomena once more to have been alive. Thus the renaissance of science was of necessity and in fact preceded by a renaissance of curiosity.[2]

RATIONALISM AT THE RENAISSANCE AND AFTER

The revival of science was not due to or accompanied by any corresponding decline in rationalism. The giants of the Renaissance appear to have been untroubled by any suspicion that reason was not the ultimate arbiter

---

[1] The *De fabrica corporis humani* of Andreas Vesalius and the *De revolutionibus orbium celestium* of Nicolaus Copernicus.

[2] Singer, Charles; *Studies in the History and Method of Science*, vol. ii.

of truth. The symmetry, the acceptability, in short the reasonableness, of a doctrine still seemed the major and final evidence of its truth. No doubt had arisen of the assumption that the sense of rationality corresponds with a similar order in the outer world. Medical theory could still base itself on the four elements, the four humours, and the four temperaments as fundamental truths; and it was long before astronomy ceased to prove that the orbit of a planet must be a circle because that is the perfect curve. All that had happened was that facts had re-established their birthright. There were no qualms about how troublesome these upstarts were likely to become. They were, of course, to prove a decisive factor in the situation.

From the time of the Renaissance the accumulation of fact was to proceed at first with a moderate, but at length with an overwhelming acceleration. The faith in reason underwent no debilitation from within, but began to suffer a certain dilapidating erosion from without. Rationalism lost its scholastic severity and perhaps gained thereby in attractiveness. The change introduces us to a third period in its evolution, which in contrast with the ingenuous rationalism of the Greeks and the austere rationalism of the Middle Ages we might call latitudinarian. By this time medicine had become distinct enough for us to consider it more or less apart from science in general. We have reached the period lying between the massive discoveries associated with the names of Vesalius, Servetus, and Harvey, on the one hand, and the not less revolutionary work of Pasteur and Lister on the other. Here we have a stretch of roughly 200 years, comprising the eighteenth and about half of each of the adjacent centuries. Discovery, of course, proceeded actively throughout this time, and the accumulation of knowledge soon became enormous. The causation of disease was still obscure, for no single fundamental element of it had been established. The field therefore was as free to the theorist as it had been in ancient Greece, but there were two fresh elements. These were, first, the now very great store of facts, and, secondly, the decline in rationalistic rigour.

The characteristic feature of the period was the exuberance with which doctrine flourished. Almost every eminent medical personage—who might well at the same time be making solid contributions of fact to medicine—was the exponent of a theoretical system of disease. This system, devised by its inventor according to some inspirational method of his own, was often as detached from reality as it was precise and dogmatic. It is impossible to review the innumerable systems that sprang into life and often so surprisingly survived; I can only mention a few names taken almost at random from Garrison's well-known work,[1] and trust to be able to convey some of the quality of their doctrines.

Early in our period there is Georg Ernst Stahl, whose life almost exactly corresponds with the interval between the death of Harvey and the birth of Hunter. He taught an animism which regarded the body as a mechanical puppet, whose functions were maintained by the direct action of the soul. Misbehaviour of the soul was therefore the cause of bodily disease. It seemed to be a necessary consequence of this theory that drugs could have no action on the body, and like a good rationalist Stahl denied that they had. His responsibility for the many animists and vitalists who followed him is perhaps less heavy than for the phlogiston theory with which he burdened chemists, for this theory is perhaps the most

[1] Garrison, Fielding H.: *An Introduction to the History of Medicine*.

perfect example in the world of ideas of the mysterious viability of the false. Then there is John Brown, whose life coincides roughly in time with that of Hunter, and who was the author of the famous Brunonian system. This product of reason is said to have been remarkably complete and consistent; it divided diseases into sthenic and asthenic, and treated them respectively with opium and alcohol, drugs to which Brown himself, less tough than his system, early succumbed.

The air of caricature never fails to show itself in the products of reason applied relentlessly and without correction. The observation of clinical facts would seem to be a pursuit of the physician as harmless as it is indispensable. Reason, however, could scarcely stop at so elementary a phase as this, and it seemed irresistibly rational to certain minds that diseases should be as fully classifiable as are beetles and butterflies. This doctrine found its most eminent cultivator in the great Sydenham, but bore perhaps its richest fruit in the hands of Boissier de Sauvages. In his *Nosologia Methodica*, published in 1768, the year of Hunter's appointment to St. George's, this Linnaeus of the bedside grouped diseases into ten classes, 295 genera, and 2,400 species. Towards the end of our period these particular developments met an opponent in Broussais, who lived till Lister was 11 and Pasteur 16. For Broussais disease in the sense of the nosologist had no existence. Diseases were for him consequences of local irritation and resulted in gastro-enteritis, which was the essential pathological lesion of all maladies. Broussais's quality is shown by his aphorism *La nature n'a aucun pouvoir de guérison naturelle*: believing this, he knew that recovery depended solely on the exertions of the physician. Since the condition he had to contend with was always an irritation and could be met by reducing the patient, he set himself to starve and bleed with a dreadful rigour. The lapse of a hundred years has made this doctrine seem no more than gruesome balderdash, but it was not without plausibility for the contemporary world. In fact, no less a surgeon than the great Dupuytren was a believer, and was accustomed to add to his mere surgical powers of reducing his patients the sterner measures of his colleague.

If these instances give a fair sample of what the intellect was doing for medicine for 200 years, it is not perhaps surprising to find Hunter about the middle of that period exclaiming impatiently, 'Why think?'

The Decline of Rationalism in Medicine

When we pass on to consider the state of affairs that obtains at present the first thing that strikes us is that no one is likely to make that exclamation now. I can imagine no reproach less likely to be needed. A reorientation has occurred towards what can be done by rational speculation for the advancement of knowledge. We can scarcely bring ourselves to listen to anyone who is not actually engaged in investigating facts, and to call an author speculative is a severe censure.

This change has been the result not of deliberate choice but of the pressure of circumstances. These circumstances have been the overwhelming success of the method of experiment in recent times, and the fabulous rate at which the accumulation of ascertained fact has progressed. There can be no reasonable doubt that the decline in the influence of rational speculation has coincided with a period in which the increase of knowledge has been rapid beyond example. Even if we can be sure, as I think we can, that the increase of knowledge was in no sense caused by the decline in speculation, we are left with but another confirmation of a conclusion that has become increasingly clear throughout this discussion. That conclusion is that at no time right up to the present day has medical doctrine borne any close and functional relation with medical discovery. If we handle this rule without trying to enforce it absolutely, and with a reasonable breadth of interpretation, we shall find it applies to every period of medical history. Although this conception is not generally and consciously recognized, and as far as I know has never even been specifically enunciated, it has long been acted on both in medicine and in science. There can therefore be no purpose in failing to admit that, in general, discovery has been the result of action rather than of thought. Fact has led to fact, observation to observation, experiment to experiment; and there has been little or no long-range guidance from rational contemplation and foresight. The relation of doctrine and discovery has not only been without co-operation, it has often been hostile; for the progress of knowledge has again and again been arrested or embarrassed by supposedly rational arguments and accepted principles. The historian is apt to be indignant at the obstacles to new knowledge offered by the censure of theologians and the persecution of ecclesiastics. Theologian and ecclesiastic have no doubt done their best, but the effect of their utmost zeal has been insignificant in comparison with that resulting from the conscientious use of the rational mind.

THE FUNCTION OF RATIONAL THOUGHT IN MEDICINE

If we accept the view that the cultivation of the theoretical side of medicine has on the whole delayed progress, should we not rejoice in the fact that that kind of study has been almost wholly destroyed by the pressure of experiment and its great success? In that case we should be able to give a definite answer to the Hunterian interrogation with which I began. Why think? Why indeed! The situation, however, is not quite so simple as to be settled in that way, and there are at least two strong reasons why a permanent abeyance of the theoretical, speculative, and rational element in the pursuit of medicine could not be regarded as wholly satisfactory.

In the first place experience seems to show that a branch of knowledge strictly limited to experiment and without any kind of speculative admixture tends in time to lose its inspiration and drift into a dry and rigid orthodoxy. Some such decline was perceptible in the physical sciences towards the end of the nineteenth century, and there can be little doubt that a strict reliance on experiment alone would in the long run have a similar deadening effect on scientific medicine. In the second place medicine is, as we shall point out more fully later, a composite subject. One of its elements is an experimental science, but a large part of it obeys the very different discipline of a practical art. In consequence it has often to deal with and act upon incompletely definable situations, and to develop the faculty of practical judgement on imperfect evidence—an activity characteristically absent from an experimental science. As long, therefore, as medicine continues to be so largely an activity of a non-scientific kind, every faculty of the active, rational mind is to be desired in the practice of it. But as we have already been at pains to point out, the exercise of the rational mind in the attempt to integrate and theorize medicine has been abundantly tried, and has always proved singularly ineffective, if not harmful.

The issue from this dilemma is a very obvious one,

although one which there seems to be a strange disinclination to take. It lies in dispersing the delusion that practical thought is easy, needs no training or precaution, and is available forthwith for anyone who turns his mind to it. Psychology has shown how little these expectations are likely to be realized, but it has not accepted the complementary duty on the positive side of producing a definite method of elementary instruction in effective thought. Among the reproaches, just and unjust, to which that science is exposed this is one of the more serious, that it has failed to show us by precept, and especially perhaps by example, how to think. It would be presumptuous in me to pretend to the ability even to enter on such a task, but one or two fundamental principles may be mentioned as the more obvious of the foundations of such an undertaking.

The physical organs and aptitudes of the body do their work only under definite conditions, and in using them no one doubts the need for practice and for acquiring a sound technique. The intellect, on the other hand, seems to its user to be an apparatus already perfected, needing no exercise or instruction, but sprung into being ready to carry out its functions without flaw or friction. In actual fact it is as much a biological product as the bodily organs, and subject to similar conditioned functioning; it is as squeamish in its way as the stomach, and as selective as the kidney or choroid plexus. Some of the restrictions on the working of the rational mind are probably structural and therefore inveterate, like the inability to conceive space in more than three dimensions and possibly others we do not even suspect. The practically important ones, however, are functional, and can be reduced or in some degree eluded through awareness and training. It is a rather crude but substantially true description of these obstacles to free thought to say they are all due, more or less directly, to the interpenetration of all thinking—even the most completely abstract—by the needs, the fears, the wishes of the thinker. The dispassionate intellect, the open mind, the unprejudiced observer, exist in an exact sense only in a sort of intellectualist folk-lore; states even approaching them cannot be reached without a moral and emotional effort most of us cannot or will not make. There are few terms in such deep disgrace nowadays as altruism, and perhaps justly so, for it has been the excuse for a good deal of silliness. Nevertheless, something in the nature of altruism in the plain sense of the word and with no mystical implication is necessary for effective thought. For there can be no approach to truth without some threat to the thinker's personality.

Simple Tasks for Thought in Medicine

Happily these altitudes are as much beyond my theme as beyond my capacity, and I turn with relief to a humbler task. We shall probably all agree that medicine permits and calls for a great deal of practical thinking. The first topic that suggests itself as in some special need of sound and rational doctrine happens also to be the most elementary; it is that of the fundamental definition of what precisely medicine and the work of the doctor are. We are much concerned nowadays about medical education and the designing of curricula. It would appear that fundamental to all such considerations should be clear conceptions of the nature of the subject itself. This is particularly necessary and a little difficult because the subject is a composite one, and considerations very relevant to one of its elements are apt to be confusing if inadvertently applied to another. The constituents of which medicine is made up are readily discernible; they are three—a practical art, an applied science, and an experimental science.

MEDICINE AS A PRACTICAL ART

It is always readily agreed that medicine is an art. The indispensable task of defining precisely what that phrase means is, however, less frequently undertaken. Medicine is a practical art in the same sense as is the work of the farmer, the smith, or the joiner. When this primary stage of definition is reached it becomes clear that definite qualities and modes of activity must be possessed by this element in medicine. These are of great practical importance, and it is surprising that they have had little exact notice. Now that the prestige of science is so high the statement that a great part of medicine still retains the status of an art is often made with a note of apology. Nothing could be less justified by a realistic sense of cultural values. The method of the practical art was the first instrument forged by man for the subjugation of chaos. At the dawn of civilization the preservation of knowledge was far more important than its discovery. The accidental fruits of experience and the creations of genius could be saved from an infallible oblivion only by being preserved in the precepts and tradition of a practical art. The superlative need for preservation made the arts inherently conservative, for there was, and is, no unequivocal difference between the change that was progress and the change that was decay. New knowledge was therefore accepted as reluctantly as old custom was given up.

An art carries its possessions in precepts and rule of thumb which are applied to individual cases in the light of a trained judgement. It does not possess principles of general validity automatically applicable: that is the method of applied science. An art is taught first in precepts and rules, secondly in experience of its material, and thirdly—and most important—by example. The method of apprenticeship is thus the keynote of education in the practical arts, because it brings the pupil into familiar contact with his material and gives him the constant example of his teacher in the actual things he himself will ultimately have to do. English medical education has long been recognized as having a characteristic product. This quality, whether we regard it as good or bad, has been due to medicine being regarded as essentially a practical art, and to the consequent predominance of apprenticeship in some form as an educational method.

If we have grasped correctly the nature of the practical arts we shall be able to specify to some extent the attitude of mind and the kind of thinking necessary for the satisfactory practice of them. It is commonly said that one of the chief objects of medical education should be to make the student think scientifically. The saying is perhaps as good an example as could be found of the need in which medicine stands for the exercise of the critical mind. To think scientifically may be supposed to mean one of two things. First, it may signify the adoption of a general habit of thought induced in, and characteristic of, those who practise experimental science. Unfortunately, however, it is not possible to show that the scientific worker outside his job displays more wisdom, insight, and practical judgement than anyone else of the same general capacity. Secondly, to think scientifically may mean to use the kind of mental process necessary for the satisfactory pursuit of experimental science. The scientific worker among other qualities must have an especially severe standard of evidence and proof; he must draw no conclusion that is not strictly justified by the evidence, and he must be content to leave in suspense any decision for which the materials are not quite complete. Now the last thing a doctor is free to do is to exercise the scientific suspense of judgement, and he scarcely ever makes a decision that is justifiable on strictly scientific grounds. The advice to think scientifically would seem, therefore, to risk paralysing his judgement rather than activating it.

The truth appears to be that what the user of a practical art needs is less the strict and limited instrument of scientific method than what may be called a soundly cultivated judgement. This requirement is more difficult to specify and much more difficult to secure. Apart from inborn capacity, it seems to depend on familiarity with the material of the art, otherwise experience, and on a broad and sound general culture which, while including a proper awareness of science, is by no means limited to it. The ancient and honourable art of medicine is being increasingly and inevitably pressed on by applied science, and suffers as well from misunderstanding and loss of prestige. It remains, however, the backbone of medical practice and indispensable to mankind. There is therefore an especial need to-day that its characteristic mode of activity should be understood, and should not be confused with those of the other elements that make up the complex of medicine.

MEDICINE AS APPLIED SCIENCE

The conversion of the practical arts into applied sciences is a characteristic and familiar process in modern civilization. The rate at which this change is going on is often the subject of enthusiastic and even excited comment. To the sober realist, however, it is clear that the rule of science in medicine is still not much more than strictly local and much qualified. The cases are very few in which general principles can be applied to the individual instance with the direct precision of an engineer designing a dynamo. The diagnosis and treatment of errors of refraction, certain cases of bacteriological and of chemical diagnosis, and others of physical diagnosis and treatment, with the dietetic deficiencies, make up the examples of nearly pure applied science. Elsewhere methods of precision must be very strictly subject to the art of medicine if they are not to become a mere snare. The affectation of scientific exactitude in circumstances where it has no meaning is perhaps the fallacy of method to which medicine is now most exposed. When we observe how fully the quack has assimilated the language of science it is easy to see the need for exact definitions lest we ourselves fall, with the worthiest intentions, into something not much better.

Medicine as an Experimental Science

When we turn to contemplate the element of experimental science in medicine, we find that the need for some effort of definition is not less than it is elsewhere. Experimental medicine, or, as it has been more conveniently named, clinical science, is at a stage when the clear recognition of it as an independent form of scientific activity—if such it really is—is peculiarly important. If it is a science capable of being pursued and developed as such, it is a competitor for support on equal terms with the other sciences, and occupies a field particularly likely to attract endowment.

Now it is often supposed that the case for the independence of clinical science is met by pointing out that the scientific element in medicine is merely applied physiology and applied pathology. From this not very recondite truth it is concluded that any further benefit to medicine from physiological and pathological discovery can come only from work done by professed physiologists and pathologists. This view seems to ignore the way in which the sciences are distributed and have come into being. Independent sciences have arisen in the past, not apparently according to whether people said they must or they must not, but through finding a natural field and doing good work in it. According to their fields of work the sciences can be divided in a broad and simplified way into two groups. There are what we may call the *general* sciences, such as physics and chemistry, by which phenomena of a certain *kind* are chosen for study. Then there are the sciences we may call *topical*, by which phenomena of a certain *distribution* are chosen for study. Belonging to the second group are such sciences as astronomy, meteorology, and geology. The fact that they could all be described as applied physics and chemistry does not in the least impair their continued independence. These sciences have readily assimilated new discoveries in physics and chemistry that were relevant to their work. They have, however, not been content merely to wait on progress in these sciences, but have been ready to undertake physical and chemical researches on their own account in problems presented by their material, and often with the happiest results. It is certain that meteorology and geology would not be in their present healthy state if they had not been prepared boldly to invade the realm of the physicist or chemist when occasion arose.

The analogy between the position of these disciplines and that of clinical science is close and instructive.

Clinical science takes as its field the study of sick people, thus choosing a range of phenomena forming a natural group of the highest importance and interest, and no more arbitrary from the theoretical point of view than are those chosen by the meteorologist and geologist. The chief sciences that are general in the sense we have defined in regard to clinical science are physiology and pathology. While taking full advantage of any appropriate discovery in these sciences, it need no more wait on the advance of them than geology has waited on the advance of physics and chemistry, but is bound to undertake physiological and pathological researches of its own when they become relevant to its purpose. The art of medicine will long remain the chief implement of the practical doctor. Admirably adapted as it is for the conservation of knowledge it is in its very nature ill suited for the discovery of new truth. I venture, in conclusion, to recall a classical example of this fact and its consequences.

In 1745 James Lind described the cure of scurvy by lemon juice; and in 1840 Steinhaeuser that of rickets by cod-liver oil. If these doctrines had been enunciated by teachers of great prestige they might have become accepted clinical precepts and slowly acquired empirical stability. They did not have that good fortune. In spite of the desperate urgency of the problem of scurvy in the eighteenth century, and that of rickets in the nineteenth, no proof or disproof was established, because it is not in the nature of a practical art to seek for certainty in the scientific sense. The truth remained undistinguished among the innumerable opinions current about these diseases for 150 years in one case and eighty years in the other. As late as the admirable *Encyclopaedia Britannica* of 1911, the most authoritative opinion inclined to ascribe rickets to an intestinal toxin and scurvy to an unknown microbe. The practical art of medicine alone knew the urgency of the problems, and actually for many years possessed the key to both. It was therefore in an extraordinarily favourable position for a direct attack on them. The method alone it, as an art, did not and could not possess. That belonged to physiology, which for long years had no interest in the problems, and approached them at last as it were indirectly and almost with reluctance. When the cause of scurvy was at last scientifically ascertained in the classical experiments of Holst and Fröhlich two circumstances of the discovery attract our notice. It was made 173 years after Bachstrom had categorically and correctly announced the cause of scurvy and 162 years after Lind had described its cure, and it was made in the course of a research primarily undertaken for another purpose. It is difficult not to believe than an active clinical science, by its situation so favourably placed for a direct attack, could have saved some of these long and costly years.

HAS THE INTELLECT A FUNCTION?[1]

THERE is no aspiration more commonly expressed by conscientious teachers than that they should be able to give their pupils the power to think for themselves. This ambition seems so innocent and laudable that we are apt to let it pass without examining its merits as a practical proposition. If we do look at it closely in that light we cannot fail to notice certain unexpected features about it. One is that those who propose to confer this great gift of free thought often manifest but little of that activity themselves. A second is that when a pupil does by chance show some evidence of individual thinking the teacher himself is apt to seem a little disconcerted; but perhaps the oddest thing that is noticeable in these good intentions is a reticence about how they are to be carried out. Pupils are to be taught to think for themselves but how it is to be done is withheld from us.

I have produced this little problem merely as an introductory note. Before passing on, however, we may extract from it a more general reference. We have before us the assumption that the exercise of thinking— and especially of independent thinking—is beyond all question good and desirable. But we also find that this approval is not in practice so wholly unqualified as seems at first to appear. I have called to mind the fact that in the rare case of a pupil developing independence of thought even the teacher is apt to show as a little taken aback. We have the hint, then, that our general applause for thinking is not without an eye on what is thought;

[1] A lecture given at the Institute of Pathology, St. Mary's Hospital, 20 June 1939. Reprinted from the *Lancet*, 24 June 1939, p. 1419.

that when we urge the young to think for themselves we are inclined to be disappointed if they do not think like us. At the climax of *Mansfield Park* we become aware of some anxiety lest the amiable inertia of Lady Bertram should prevent her reacting to the elopement of her married daughter with the proper indignation. We are reassured, however, by this remark of the author: 'Lady Bertram did not think deeply but, guided by Sir Thomas, she thought justly on all important points.' It is to be feared that when we desire our pupils to think for themselves our anxiety is not so much that they should think deeply as that they should think justly on all important points.

The Problem Itself

These trivial preliminary reflections serve to bring us without undue abruptness into the presence of our actual problem, which is the behaviour of the faculty of reason in man. Without pausing here to fidget with definitions it is necessary to say that I use this expression—faculty of reason—which is now so old-fashioned as to be practically out of work, to denote in a broad rough way the capacities in which man differs from the other animals. Now the faculty of reason in one aspect may be said to be the indispensable agent in everything man has accomplished. It enables him to learn, to add knowledge to knowledge and preserve it, to build up arts, sciences, and civilizations without limit. Yet, in another aspect, this same implement can as it were, turn in his hand and become the enemy of all constructive activities. With its Ptolemaic systems, caloric fluids, and phlogiston theories, reason has been deleterious enough even in the quiet fields of science. It taught astronomers that planetary orbits are circular because the circle is the perfect curve; it proved that the number of planets could be no more than seven and enabled Hegel to deride the none the less successful search for an eighth by Adams and Le Verrier; and even to-day it probably exercises over free experiment a quiet censorship far stronger than most of us would like to admit.

The history of medicine teaches us that when reason took a hand *there* it was not only truth that suffered. The rational system of a Stahl, a Brown, a Rush, or a Broussais unfortunately did not exist in a mere metaphysical vacuum but at the bedside—and armed with opium, antimony, alcohol, mercury, the lancet, and the purge. Thus the consequences of the confident use of reason in medicine have been gloomy enough. When the same implement has been applied to the general affairs of life the results have been even more dreadful. Few proscriptions, persecutions, and massacres but have had their reasoned and logical justification. The various systems of doctrine that have held dominion over man have been demonstrated to be true beyond all question by rationalists of such power—to name only the greatest—as Aquinas and Calvin and Hegel and Marx. Guided by these master hands the intellect has shown itself more deadly than cholera or bubonic plague and far more cruel. It is a strange fact that this pestilential virulence of reason has never fired the ambition of some great sanitarian of the mind. The incompatibility with one another of all the great systems of doctrine might surely have been expected to provoke some curiosity about their nature.

ACCEPTED SOLUTIONS

These few random instances should be enough to enforce what is after all a very old discovery. The things that come into the mind have a disarming air of obviousness and certainty. But it must have been known at a very early period that they are not to be taken for what they seem without some corrective test of their validity, and some other authentication than their own charm.

In the agelong struggle with this problem no solution has been found that has been able to make human reason a universally applicable and generally trustworthy implement. Nevertheless something has come out of the struggle. This has been the evolution of three methods of setting about the pursuit of knowledge. They are not sharply marked off from one another and tend a good deal to overlap the limits one may be tempted to define for them. They do, however, clearly differ in the aspect of their task on which each lays its chief emphasis. Of these three methods the first is that of the practical art, which is mainly directed to the preservation of knowledge; the second is that of the natural sciences, which is directed to the increase of verifiable knowledge; and the third is that of philosophy, which seeks the unification of knowledge. The objects then of these three attitudes towards experience—the rewards of man's struggle for intellectual discipline—are respectively to preserve, to verify, and to unite. What their success has been we may now inquire.

The Method of the Practical Art

The method of the practical art is that of the carpenter, the farmer, the builder, the doctor; it has, of course, as such, nothing to do with the plastic arts and the aesthetic, but it may well excite our reverence as perhaps embodying the fundamental intellectual discovery on which all civilizations have been built up. Its primary interests have always been the preservation and transmission of knowledge rather than its discovery. These characters have made it the nurse of civilization at a time when a new discovery could survive only by being fixed in the tradition of an art. A practical art comes then in its very nature to be strongly conservative, reluctant to accept the new, still more reluctant to give up the old; it will teach by precept and example of the master, by apprenticeship; it will embody its lore in traditional dogma and in rule of thumb. Its ideal of success will thus be fulfilled as much by a given course of conduct having been correctly carried out as by its object having been attained. If he knows that he has proceeded *secundum artem* the practitioner will not be greatly distressed by a mere lack of success; and will readily blame the weather for the failure of his crop, the materials for the collapse of his building, and his patients' constitutions for their diseases.

The extended reasoning process has little function in the practical arts. If allowed to enter them it finds itself in an environment possessing no indigenous methods of controlling it and is apt to develop a harmful exuberance. Nothing could illustrate this principle better than the speculative systems that devastated the medicine of the eighteenth and early nineteenth centuries in the way I have already referred to. To maintain its health a practical art must be sparing of theory and keep closely in contact with facts. It has no method of discovery other than that of almost purely random trial and error; it has no characteristic method of proof and can assimilate truth only when the prestige of its discoverer is great. For example, Steinhaeuser might discover in 1840, and Hughes Bennett proclaim, that cod-liver oil cures rickets, but this enormously important fact remained unproved and no more than a not very respectable pious opinion for the next eighty years.

THE METHOD OF THE NATURAL SCIENCES

The second of what I have called the three methods of setting about the pursuit of knowledge is that of the natural sciences. We need not attempt a complete definition of natural science, and if we were to try we should find that its margins tend to grow indistinct as we concentrate on them. A perfectly adequate practical definition is the statement that its central function is to acquire verifiable knowledge. A verifiable fact is one that has shown itself to have a relation to certain definable conditions such that wherever and whenever the conditions have been reproduced the fact in question has always accompanied them. Such verification is the characteristic and only sanction of science. Whether we like a given fact or not, and whether it seems true or revolts our reason, are quite irrelevant to its scientific validity.

All knowledge comes from noticing resemblances and recurrences in the events that happen around us. Although some of us may be much quicker than others in the power of seeing and comparing, it is obvious that the greatest talent cannot carry us very far as long as observation and experiment are applied only to random experience. It is the discovery of natural science that experience can be simplified so that on the one hand resemblances and recurrences in events can be more easily seen, and on the other that the conditions in which they occur can be completely specified. This, using the term in the broadest sense, is the experimental method. In one aspect it may be regarded as a mere refinement of the rough and ready trial and error of the craftsman and the common man. In another aspect, however, the change is so great as to be virtually a qualitative one and to make the method distinct from all others. It is not necessary to dilate here on the power it has displayed in advancing knowledge or the huge acceleration it has imparted to that process. It is more relevant to note the limits to which its application is subject. The scientific method is unfitted to tackle directly the turbulent stream of everyday experience and common affairs; it must run off minute fractions of it into carefully specified and engineered channels before it can bring its powers to bear. Thus, for example, the work of social government is not as such directly accessible to it on account of the jumbled miscellaneity of the matters involved.

In saying this I must guard myself against being thought to pronounce on a wholly different question which might be supposed to be similar. It is, of course, obvious that governments now existing fail to make use of much knowledge already established by science and capable of immediate application. Even, however, if this deplorable lag could be abolished, the direct application of scientific method to government itself as a whole would, with our present powers, be impossible.

After what has been to some extent a digression we pick up the line of our argument again when we ask ourselves what part in the scientific method is taken by what I have called the extended reasoning process. The history of science is generally supposed to furnish a wonderful display of the triumphs of human reason. I must confess that the reading of it does not induce in me any such grandiose conception of the mind. The separate steps of progress have rarely been much prepared for by long flights of rational forecast. Great investigators seem mostly to have been led from fact to fact; to have depended on a kind of intuitive flair for the behaviour of their material; and to have used reasoning rather for the planning of their work and the design of experiments than for elaborate structures of argument.

Although rational and imaginative speculation is of the greatest general value to science in keeping it from going dry and orthodox, as an actual implement of research it has not very much to its credit. Experience has shown time and again that as soon as science leaves immediate contact with the facts it begins to lose direction and reality, and must constantly return to them for orientation. Great discoveries will therefore continue to be unexpected and the advance of science occur on an irregular front in which the salients mark the places where amongst the facts the going is good. Even research deliberately directed against short-range targets is apt to be held up contrary to all reasonable expectation or to score its successes through unintentional deflections. In the light of these considerations we may contemplate with benefit the bitter war of attrition that has marked the enormous and world-wide attack on cancer; or remember Rayleigh setting out to determine the atomic weight of nitrogen and coming up against argon, or Holst and Fröhlich setting out to study beri-beri and finding the cause of scurvy. We thus seem to get the plain hint of a rather odd conclusion. It is that natural science—by far the most successful of man's inventions for setting about the pursuit of knowledge— has not been able to make any extended use of the directive faculty of reason. If we were to allow the sceptical spirit full liberty for a moment, we might find ourselves wondering whether the vast mass of scientific knowledge has not in some queer way invented itself— a suggestion that makes it seemly to change the subject.

The Method of Philosophy

The third method of setting about the pursuit of knowledge is that of philosophy. We may content ourselves here by defining philosophy no more closely than to say it has for its central object the search for unification or less summarily the effort to bring all knowledge whatever into a single consistent scheme. We have perhaps been a little disconcerted at finding ourselves able at least to defend the view that the rational activities of the mind have played no overwhelming part in the practical arts or the natural sciences. We shall not have that fault—if it is a fault—to find with philosophy.

As far as history is able to tell us, the deliberate use of rational thought as an implement of research was invented by the Greeks of classical times some 2,500 years or more ago. It is difficult to think of now as a definite discovery and to call it such sounds like calling locomotion or digestion a discovery. Nevertheless it was a true discovery and produced a real deflection in the strange roads of human destiny. We can call a discovery great when it catches man unprepared, and we find in the history of many such the evidence of man's unpreparedness in the way he has tended to mix the use and misuse of these gifts. Rational thought in the pursuit of knowledge bears these marks of mixed use and misuse as plainly as do printing, gunpowder, and the internal-combustion engine.

This new implement was to impel intellectual activity into a course it was to follow for two and a half millennia. We may therefore well ask ourselves what precisely was the device that could exercise so strong an influence. It was abstract thought. At that name of power we find ourselves at last compelled to devise an exact definition.

The discovery that was made by the Greek, and that

we may fairly say intoxicated him, was that you can consider the qualities of things apart from the things themselves. You survey, let us suppose, a miscellaneous collection of objects, untidy and with no coherent meaning. Suddenly you notice that they possess in common some such quality as hardness or colour or weight, and that you can think of this as existing apart from the disorderly mess you are looking at. A new thing has appeared—an abstraction—having an existence of its own and superior to the accidents of the apparent world. You find that these abstractions are easy to think about. They are clear, shapely, and can be depended on to stay where you put them. You can consider their relations to one another at your ease without being bothered by odd and 'insignificant' individualities. No wonder its discoverers were enchanted by this method of introducing order and seemliness into the chaos of experience and that they exploited it to excess.

A good deal of mystery has been made of the fact that the Greeks, with all their curiosity and liveliness of mind, turned away so obstinately from the immediate study of nature. Even Aristotle was rather contemptuous of direct observation and experiment, and Plato says somewhere concerning the study of natural phenomena, 'these things have no absolute first principle and can never be the objects of reason and true science'. The mystery seems to me rather artificial. The Greeks despised the mere pedestrian grubbing among facts because they had discovered something superior to it. In the abstract world they had found a better kind of reality —orderly, clean, unaccidental, and capable of being successfully manipulated without soiling a gentleman's fingers or compromising his dignity.

It must be admitted fully that the abstract method is

ineradicably entwined in all our thinking and is indispensable. This is, however, by no means to acquiesce in its universal dominance or to excuse the general failure to examine sceptically its nature and limitations.

The charm and the use of the method are that it permits us to take into our minds phenomena in their essence only, to examine them there, and as it were acquire experience of them without being distracted by their mere individual oddities. The abstraction 'space' thus comes to represent a certain common quality of innumerable experiences in the world of corners, surfaces, heights, depths, and breadths. Vertebrate, amphibian, man are the well-behaved substitutes of countless creatures creeping, jumping, and running about the world in their odd unaccountable way. This process of abstracting what I have rather light-heartedly called the essence of phenomena, will be found to reward a rather closer attention and such attention may well be directed first to the simplest case of the process.

Remarkably little attention seems to have been given to the important fact that the only quality we know of which can be *completely* abstracted is number. Five digits in the mind are, as regards number, as good as five fingers of the hand. Every numerical experience of them and every such manifestation of them that is possible in the outer world can be initiated or repeated in the mind and with equal validity. The science of positive numbers is then the science which is at once perfectly abstract and perfectly experimental. The moment we leave number there begins to appear a decline in the exactitude of the correspondence between the abstraction and the reality. For a long time it seemed that the qualities of space could also be completely abstracted because the conclusions derived from the abstract consideration of space seemed to be confirmed everywhere in the outer world, even on the astronomical scale. Ultimately, however, it dawned on the geometers that there is a discrepancy between the abstraction and the reality. The need of an Einstein to point this out and the uproar that followed are perhaps a little surprising to mere common sense. What seems truly remarkable is not that intuitions derived from the stretch of the arms and the range of the eye should ultimately break down, but that their validity is so wide and their error so small.

When we apply the abstract method to events of the living world as we constantly do and must, we find ourselves faced by a great increase in the individuality of phenomena and should be prepared for a sudden drop in the representative value of all abstractions. The abstraction 'man' must always be a thin, imperfect, and easily misleading summary of the innumerable individual 'men'. It is in the world of ideas, however, that the abstract makes its highest flights and develops to the full its fascinations and its dangers. Truth, justice, honour, beauty, being, right, wrong; I give a mere random list of abstractions from that world. These are no mere manageable equivalents designed for convenience of thought. They are creations which, made in all innocence, have taken on a life of their own and become the rulers of the mind. Could there be a more plausible and useful-looking conception than that of 'truth'—a unitary principle that is to be the ultimate sanction at once of the statesman and the theologian, the man of science and the poet? Yet it is easy to make out that such a supposed unity can never be, and that behind its solemn frontage is a mere jumble of ideas. Nevertheless this bogus unit has notoriously had a strange power over man's mind and proved itself to be perhaps the most disastrous idol he has ever set up.

Abstraction of some degree is universal and inveterate in all kinds of thinking; in philosophic thinking, however, it is in addition characteristic and indispensable. The aim of philosophy is to unify all knowledge; it must therefore seek the generality it supposes to lie behind the multitudinous particulars of experience. In thus separating reality from its accidents it must depend on the abstract method as its instrument and on reason as its sanction. Things will be true when they are pronounced true by the informed and enlightened intellect. The ultimate standard of philosophic truth is therefore an internal one; in the last resort such a truth is one that 'feels true' to the philosopher. Philosophy has been cultivated by many, perhaps even most of the ablest minds the human race has produced. It has evolved innumerable systems of doctrine, each rationally proved by its founder to be true, and all inconsistent with one another. No enterprise has ever been longer or better pursued than 'the effort to find a body of philosophic doctrine which should compel the universal assent of rational minds. An experiment that has gone on failing for two and a half millennia may well make us wonder whether the apparatus is adequate or the method sound.

SCIENCE AND PHILOSOPHY IN CONTRAST

The rough definitions I have tried to make of the scientific and philosophic methods should now permit us to bring the two into useful comparison with one another. Before doing so, however, it is necessary to have clearly in mind that in practice the two procedures are by no means always kept distinct. Many a supposedly scientific opinion gets itself supported on purely rational grounds, and many a philosophic conclusion affects to depend on verification. We are concerned here with the characteristic quality of the two methods, and the fact that in actual use they are often confused only adds to the need for clear definition. Philosophy then desires its conclusions to feel true, science that they should come true; philosophy needs certitude, science needs verification. Science has no certitudes because its conclusions are based not at all on internal conviction but wholly on the regularities of observed experience.

It seems at first sight a very hard saying that science has no certitudes. In face of it we may expect to be reminded that the precision and trustworthiness of science are its very essence. These are undoubtedly among its most attractive characters, but they do not depend on the complete inner conviction of truth that alone gives the sense of certitude. Science makes great use of reason in its special way; it often appeals to the rationality of its conclusions in confirmation of them; and most of its conclusions do in fact come ultimately to seem profoundly reasonable. Nevertheless it does not possess, and should not claim to be based on, a fundamental rationality; the conception that the order or rationality of the universe tallies with the order or rationality of the best human minds, while it is for philosophy a vital necessity, is for science no more than a useful working hypothesis and therefore the servant rather than the master of research. Expositors of science, however, have unfortunately sometimes tended to drift into the philosophic mood. On such occasions they are apt to tell us of the august and inflexible uniformities of nature, the iron laws of cause and effect, the inevitable certainties of science and similar rationalistic dreams. If we examine science more realistically we shall find that its two most impressive aspects are first its detailed trustworthiness in practice, and secondly its *provisional quality*. It is in this second and rather un-obtrusive character that the essence of natural science is revealed. The man of science within his own, often narrow, department can cheerfully regard all his know-ledge as provisional only, and indefinitely liable to sub-version by further inquiry. He gives us our only hope that some day the human spirit may learn to distrust all certitude, and live bravely in its own right and its own strength.

While it is to be insisted on that rationality is not the ultimate test of scientific truth, there is no reason to question the value of the rational process as an imple-ment of research. It is, however, an implement of which no finding can be regarded as valid until it has found verification in experience. Whatever flights of reason-ing science may take, it must ever be returning to the facts for reassurance. Even in the most extended feats of pioneering in the light of theory—as, for example, we see in some degree in the evolution of the thermionic valve—there must be this repeated verification of actual experiment. The wings given to science by reason must be used like those of the ostrich rather than like those of the eagle, and help it along without raising it from the solid earth.

Philosophy, on the other hand, is characteristically free from these scruples about the validity of the most extended processes of reasoning. It insists, of course, that reason must be correctly used, but with this restric-tion, inflexibly maintains its ultimate validity. I need not repeat the pessimistic conclusion we have been com-pelled to draw from the failure of philosophy to yield any single dominating system of doctrine. But it is

necessary to notice the even more formidable attack on
the ultimate validity of reason made by modern psychology. To the rationalist the intellect presents itself
as a perfect instrument; if its material is prepared for
it by competent logic, precise definition, and a proper
awareness of the difficult relations between language
and meaning, then its operations must be carried on with
frictionless integrity and its conclusions possess irre-
sistible force. I have expressed this view in its extreme
and perhaps least credible aspect. Other forms of it, less
frank but far more insidious, are so nearly general in us
all, that it should be described quite brutally as a complete delusion. To the eye of the psychologist the intellect has shown itself to be after all no more than a human
organ, with preferences and caprices like the stomach
and the kidney. Every structure of argument it builds,
however massive and symmetrical it may look, rests on
foundations from which it has no means of excluding
disturbance by bias and preconception. Under the attack
of this kind of knowledge there can be no doubt that
sooner or later the supposed independent validity of
reason must go down.

The Intellect in Daily Life

We set out on this inquiry with the innocent and
laudable idea that people should be able to think for
themselves. It has already led us rather far, so that before
allowing ourselves to be still more deeply involved we
may well ask what is to be the function of this admittedly
desirable independent thinking. It is to enable us to
contemplate usefully our current experience, and to develop opinions on social, political, and national situations
without being entirely directed by custom and by prejudice. Now it is characteristic of the experience of

daily life that it comes before us as a miscellaneous jumble of elements of which the mixture is irreducible. It must therefore be obvious that the scientific method cannot be directly applied to it since that method demands complete specification of its situations so that they may be subject to direct observation or controlled experiment. It is necessary here to guard ourselves from thinking that the practice of the scientific method enlarges the powers of the mind. Nothing is more flatly contradicted by experience than the belief that a man, distinguished in one or even several departments of science, is more likely to think sensibly about ordinary affairs than anyone else. The philosophic method, on the other hand, is no more useful for direct application in daily life than is the scientific. Its rationalism and its confident faith in abstraction would in themselves disqualify it as a guide in the real world. In judging its capacity for this part, however, we are in a stronger position than we are with regard to science. The scientific method has never been tried in public affairs; the philosophic method has been tried with a persistence and self-devotion worthy of the higher insects. Utilitarianism, Hegelianism, dialectical materialism, totalitarianism are all characteristic products of the philosophic method; however rational and self-consistent they may be, they do not seem very helpful in causing people to think for themselves.

Our search for a method that shall assist the useful contemplation of daily experience has thus had a totally negative result. The common tendency to regard destructive criticism as always easy and generally reprehensible is one that I do not share; indeed, I doubt if it could be acquiesced in by any sensible person making a frank survey of the intellectual world of to-day. We cannot but be struck by the remarkable prevalence of systems of doctrine, by their loudness, their confusion, and their deleterious effect on conduct. In all these systems the most indulgent examination will find little evidence of really enterprising thought, but it will find a great deal of reconditioned lumber, at its best of a low order of reality and now used to justify the lazier, the uglier, and the baser inclinations of the human spirit. At no time in the history of the intellect has the sanitary work of destructive criticism been more needful.

Correction of Thought

Although one might be reluctant to accept the orthodox view that destruction is justified only as a preliminary to rebuilding, we can all agree that the one is an excellent preparation for the other. If we have learnt to distrust the validity of the operations of the intellect, we at least have gained the advantage of looking at its proceedings with a new objectivity. If we have been expelled from our rationalistic paradise, at least the world is all before us where to choose.

To throw the helve after the hatchet is proverbially the temptation to which disappointment exposes us. It is not surprising, therefore, that we are sometimes advised, by what seems to be a growing body of opinion, actually to abandon the use of reason. This advice is, I suspect, more often founded on a dislike for the conclusions of reason than on any radical doubt of their validity. We possess in reason an instrument that is powerful but admittedly very awkward to handle, and apt to pinch our fingers or jump back on our shins. It seems more sensible and less pusillanimous to learn how to use it rather than to throw it away. On attempts to make the intellect a practical and handy implement a truly enormous amount of very difficult work has been done. It is almost impossible to overstate the power and the ingenuity that have been given to the study of logic and to the relations of language and meaning. What little I know of these prodigies I regard with awe, but with an uneasiness that, in spite of the best will in the world, remains incurable. Each seems to promise that with a little more polishing, a screw tightened here and a nut adjusted there, the intellect will at last have been made the perfect instrument. If, however, as I have tried to indicate, the whole instrument is subject to fundamental and incurable deflections, its operations cannot be rectified by the mere detailed adjustment of its inner machinery. Indeed the perfection of its inner mechanism may even exaggerate its total error, for no one is more commonly impenetrable to ideas than the master of dialectic.

For a good deal longer than 2,000 years the ablest men of every age have been fidgeting with the mechanism of the intellect in the hope of helping mankind to think and therefore behave reasonably. The state of the world to-day cannot but suggest that if practical thought is to become strong enough to help in saving our social systems from their increasing confusions, some more radical corrective is necessary.

The correction of instrumental errors is a familiar idea in practical science. The maker, having turned out as perfect an instrument as he knows how, studies the quality of its performance. Any error now found is to be dealt with not by tinkering with the machine but by having the constancy and amount of it carefully estimated and stated in a form that can be applied to the results. It is this method that forces itself upon us in determining the function of the intellect and rendering it fully available. Psychology has told us a great deal about the working of the mind and in an incidental way about its liabilities to error; but it has not systematically undertaken just this special practical task of, as it were, calibrating the intellect for the contemplation of ordinary experience. Unless such a work can be done it seems probable that the ominous fatuity and confusion that mark our social and political affairs must continue to increase.

We have defined our problem and indicated the direction in which its solution seems to lie. The end of so long an argument is no place to examine in detail the ways in which this solution is to be applied. It would, however, be too gross a failure in enterprise if I were not to set out in plain terms a few crude examples of such application which we can all put to use.

In the first place we must get rid of the disastrous belief that there is any activity of the mind corresponding with the conception of pure reason. The mind has no such function. All processes of reasoning, however abstract, are participated in and influenced by feeling. We cannot separate off the reasoning process as such and set it to work in an emotional vacuum. What we can do is to suspect the grosser cases of the effect of feeling and to make an appropriate correction. There are many emotional states of which the action may be so deeply masked that it is impossible to detect them at work by direct observation. Such, for example, are the influence of nationalism, religion, personal vanity, and fear—of death, of cruelty, of humiliation. Do not let us nourish the delusion that we can catch these in action and cast them out. We can tame them a little—only perhaps to make them more insidious—but even in the most dispassioned train of reasoning they are apt to exercise a steady treacherous pressure.

There is probably no commoner error than that of supposing it to be possible by a direct effort, and for the purpose of fair discussion, to free the mind from preconception and prejudice about a given question. 'Mind you I am looking at it without prejudice'; how often have all of us said that in such circumstances. It is always untrue. We should do well on these occasions to inquire closely by what precise mechanism this supernatural purgation has been effected.

We are accustomed to regard evidence as a very positive and objective thing, which we blandly pronounce conclusive or inadequate or what not in the appropriate circumstances. More reasonably science allows itself a certain amount of practical compromise and is willing for everyday purposes to accept quite a small amount of evidence for a phenomenon when it is consistent with its context. When, however, the context of a new phenomenon is thought to be incongruous, troubles are apt to arise, and perfectly respectable evidence be rejected. The history of the discovery of argon and of X-rays admirably illustrates this. On both those occasions the insidious category of 'experimental error' was able to conceal the truth for long periods—in the case of argon for no less than 100 years. Even science then shows that in practice its famous 'experimental evidence' is no infallible safeguard against preconception.

In regions where the relatively unemotional air of the laboratory does not prevail, the influence of feeling easily becomes strong enough to deprive even highly respectable bodies of evidence of any serious value. It is, for example, a curious fact that in the very full discussions of spiritualistic phenomena attention has been chiefly concentrated on the dissection of the evidence itself. To the psychologist it is meanwhile obvious that testimony, of however irreproachable an appearance, which has been collected in the atmosphere of a strong desire to believe, must as a whole be subject to such deductions that its evidential value practically vanishes.

The last I shall produce of these rather random examples of how we may set about the correction of the rational process concerns the reception of new ideas. We like to suppose ourselves easily receptive of the new, and that we are so by virtue of a natural mechanism. Unfortunately this is the exact opposite of the truth. The mind likes a strange idea as little as the body likes a strange protein, and resists it with a similar energy. It would not perhaps be too fanciful to say that a new idea is the most quickly acting antigen known to science. If we watch ourselves honestly we shall often find that we have begun to argue against a new idea even before it has been completely stated. I have no doubt that that last sentence has already met with repudiation—and shown how quickly the defence mechanism gets to work.

THE MIND IN WAR[1]
DEMOCRACY'S CHIEF ADVANTAGE

To the EDITOR OF THE TIMES

Sir,—The events of the last fortnight have strength-
ened the long gathering opinion that the adversaries in
the present war are separated not by mere political dis-
agreement but by differences in their attitude towards
life which practically amount to incompatible types of
civilization. Hostility of this sort must be, and obviously
is, exceptionally intense and inveterate, and it produces
a situation very different from the dynastic and expan-
sionary quarrels of most other wars. If the contest is of
the kind suggested it is certain that the weaker must go
to the wall and that no ultimate issue by way of compromise is likely to be possible.

That some such view of the war has been reached by
the intuitive judgement of the people is made probable
by the unanimity—perhaps unique—with which they
have accepted it. Now no sane community—particularly an old and experienced one—could enter upon a
war recognized as internecine unless it were convinced
that the system it was to fight for was not only the better
but also the stronger and more durable in all respects.
No doubt this conviction is more or less vaguely present
in most of us. It is, however, our plain duty to give it
all the definition and emphasis we can.

The democracies of this war, then, must hold to the
knowledge that the free play of mind, liberty of opinion,
and honesty are not only morally good but also sources
of every kind of strength. They must also know with
equal conviction that a selfish and exclusive nationalism

[1] *The Times*, 26 Sept. 1939.

and the patronage of cruelty, persecution, and treachery are not only base but in the long run ruinous and bear within them the seeds of death.

This strength is available to a democracy in all fields and not least in that of war. The fallacy is rather widely held that the system prevailing in Germany is necessarily pre-eminent in war. It needs no refutation in spite of our having so recently seen the German Army showing as practically omnipotent against a weaker adversary. Even there, however, the attentive observer will have noticed, it did not escape its old and highly significant malady—the *franc tireur* neurosis. The quality of the fighting forces and their material equipment do not greatly differ among the three Great Powers at war. The superiority of strength I have so confidently postulated must therefore reside in the mental world. Indeed there seems very clearly to be something in an absolutist system which, perhaps by denying the mind free play, succeeds in depriving it of some of its more vigorous and penetrating aptitudes. A good deal of German wireless propaganda seems to proceed from backward children—indeed its markedly infantile faith in the power of the mere lie is very pronounced. The incident of Ribbentrop—the world diplomatist—gabbling through the terms to Poland raises us perhaps to the level of the fourth form. Hitler's answer to the British ultimatum might have been written by a schoolboy of rather vulgar mind, and the Russian apology for the invasion of Poland was of a fatuity to which we can scarcely deny the name of innocence. I speak bluntly of these matters because I believe they reveal a certain limited but fundamental stupidity and blindness which an intelligent enemy should be able to turn to his great advantage.

Some of the kinds of strength given only by freedom

are at once obvious. We save, for example, the whole enormous material and moral expense of enforcing opinion—the secret police, the spies, the informers; and we are spared the vast platitude and boredom of enforced opinion which must always be second rate. Again, freedom has given us the means of applying external criticism to our affairs. The slowly matured organs of Parliamentary discussion and the Press are able to supply the independent, penetrating, and responsible criticism for the lack of which so many great enterprises have come to ruin.

That our superiority of strength lies chiefly in the realm of the mind is a truth of which we may suppose our rulers to be aware. They would do well, however, to bear in mind that really effective thinking is the most difficult of all human activities, and very easily inhibited by professional and official conventionalities. It is, however, more urgently needed in this war than anything else. Vigorous and original thought of an arduous kind is necessary to keep open and develop communication between Government and fighting departments and Government and people; to maintain civilian morale; to study and exploit on the largest scale the element of surprise in war; to study and exploit the advantages of contending with an enemy who has certain well-marked mental limitations, and to undertake a really serious campaign against enemy morale in supplement to the rather innocent machinations that have hitherto passed as such.

PANIC AND ITS CONSEQUENCES[1]

SOME weeks ago a few remarks of mine were printed[2] on the need for active thinking in the conduct of war. Among the subjects I named as needing attention was that of the relations between Government and people. These relations, which were at first perfect, have already shown a slight but sensible decline that must deeply concern us all. It has been said that the uses made of the great powers given to the Government by the people have not always been wise, and have sometimes been such as to stagger common sense. It is of interest therefore to call attention to an element in the general situation that may have had an influence on many of the decisions of the Government now causing dissatisfaction. As this element lay beyond the direct reach of the human will, we can discuss it without undertaking the odious task of distributing blame amongst persons who were doubtless animated by as pure a passion to serve the country as any of us.

Anyone who was in London in September and October 1938 must have been aware of something new in the moral attitude of the people. Trenches were being feverishly scratched open, many of those who could afford it were openly running away, and people of whose nerves better might have been expected confessed to an uncontrollable alarm. It was generally believed that a first-class air-raid might kill 50,000 and wound 300,000 more, that there was no real defence, and that an attack might occur at any moment. In the blackest days of 1917 and 1918 no such moral landslide was seen. The stoical

---

[1] British Medical Journal 17 Feb. 1940, p. 270 (published posthumously).
[2] *The Times*, 26 Sept. 1939.

endurance of the Londoner had gone, and in its place
was something to which the thoughtful mind could not
refuse the ominous name of panic. The weakness did
not, however, spread indefinitely. The common people
—as always the moral background of the country—
resisted and at length threw it off. But it lingered elsewhere and especially perhaps among those who also had
the heavy strain of being responsible for the safety of the
country. Innumerable critical decisions had thus to be
made by people exposed to and more or less deeply
affected by the insidious solicitations of panic. The
results of such a condition need for their understanding
no more advanced a psychological equipment than a
moderately enlightened common sense.

Man experiences two kinds of fear, which we may
call individual fear and panic fear. Of the former we
need only say that it is by no means incompatible with
mental activity of the best kind, and that it is directly
related to its object. Panic fear, on the other hand, is not
directly related to its object, but is derived by its subject
from the reactions of his fellows; it is therefore, so to
say, infectious. Being an experience solely of social
creatures, it has for its function the obliteration of the
individual consciousness, which becomes merged in an
impulse shared by its fellows. It thus happens that panic,
however mild, has an immediate effect in weakening
rational judgement. Every conclusion arrived at under
its influence, however plausible it may seem in that
deceptive medium, will be corrupted by departures from
sound sense. In examining decisions reached under the
influence of panic we are not to look for blunders and
errors of judgement, for the fruits of ignorance or the
fatuity of office, but for something at once more subtle
and more characteristic. We are to look for decisions

that could have been reached only by people in whom the faculty of practical reason was actually impaired.

The hypothesis that vast air-raids were inevitable upon or even before the declaration of war was always a dubious one and rested on all its elements being greatly magnified; it also ignored the fact that the German military command, however purged of its best minds and however infatuated with *Schrecklichkeit* as an end in itself, was the best judge of short-range strategy in the world, and little likely to waste its strength on excentric blows that could not be followed up. The idea, however, was not unreasonable and certainly deserved all consideration. Nevertheless, panic insisted that a modest probability must be treated as an immediate certainty, and used the hypothetical horrors it had foretold as part of the evidence that they would occur. A total black-out was enforced without compromise or graduation or any provision for the devoted pedestrian. The consequences may well become a classical example of the staggering paradoxes that result from mixing good intentions with panic. Deaths by violence on the roads rose in the first month of the war from 500 to 1,100. Thus by sitting quietly at home Hitler's air force was able to kill 600 British citizens at a cost to itself of exactly nothing.

With all its crudities the black-out is no more than a mild example of the effects of panic. Many other instances lie about us of which it can be maintained that they embody decisions which *no normal mind in any circumstances* could have assented to. Some happily are merely grotesque. Such escapades as carting tea about the country with the effect of eluding at once both bombs and consumers, and the outbreaks of a fatuous secrecy deserve no more than a smile. But what are we to think of patients with infectious tuberculosis discharged to spread the disease; of medical practice half paralysed and medical education wholly disorganized; of the great hospitals three-quarters empty; of elementary education crippled and higher education almost at a standstill?

I have expressed belief that we should not be concerned in the distribution of blame. There is none to distribute. We have discussed a natural phenomenon and its results. If these observations have been just, certain considerations of practical importance proceed from them. The first is that decisions bearing the diagnostic marks of having been affected by panic should be reviewed without mercy or any regard for the saving of face. The second is to take to heart the fact that under the influence of panic it was possible to ignore almost completely two kinds of strength in which this country is eminent, if not unique—its capacity for courageous endurance and its principle of reasonable compromise.

PRINTED IN
GREAT BRITAIN
AT THE
UNIVERSITY PRESS
OXFORD
BY
JOHN JOHNSON
PRINTER
TO THE
UNIVERSITY